Managing People and Technological Change

John Bailey

BA MBA PhD MIPM MITD
Independent Consultant and Training Advisor in Management
Part-time Lecturer and Honorary Research Fellow,
Business School, University of the West of England

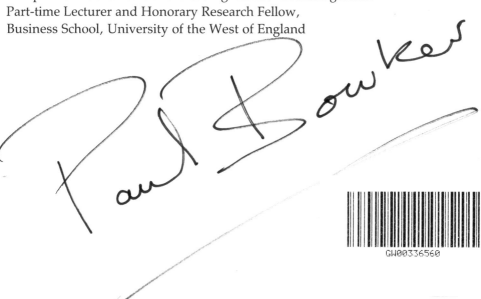

GW00336560

PITMAN
PUBLISHING

Pitman Publishing
128 Long Acre, London WC2E 9AN

A Division of Longman Group UK Limited

© J R S Bailey 1993

First published in Great Britain 1993

British Library Cataloguing in Publication Data
A catalogue record for this book is available
from the British Library

ISBN 0 273 60027 3

Printed and bound in Great Britain by
Biddles Ltd, Guildford and King's Lynn

DEDICATION

This book is dedicated to my long suffering family,
to my wife Rosemary, son Mark and daughters
Anna and Victoria, who despite my preoccupation
with the research and the book have given me
continued encouragement, interest and support.

CONTENTS

PREFACE

Since the Industrial Revolution and the introduction of scientific management, much has been learnt about human behaviour and motivation at work. Developments in the field of job design and socio-technical systems have helped us recognise the value of job satisfaction and employee involvement in achieving the goals of high productivity, quality and good customer service.

In what is often described as the Second Industrial Revolution, the question is whether we have learnt from the mistakes of the past. Does the introduction of new technology and computer systems of information and manufacture necessarily have to be at the expense of people and human involvement?

The appeal of this book will largely be in the educational field at under-graduate, postgraduate and post experience work. It will provide an important perspective on the issues involved in the introduction of new technology that will be relevant to management, business studies, computer and engineering students.

It will also be of value to the practitioner, whether manager, consultant, systems analyst, production engineer, technician, personnel specialist or trade unionist.

With its important emphasis in linking technology, job design and socio-technical systems thinking with the current interests in strategy and culture the book will have a wide appeal in courses relating not only to information technology, organisational behaviour and operations management but also in the field of business policy and strategy.

This book, which is based on the author's current research, explores the impact of new technology on people and their jobs and how, through the use of job design and work organisational development concepts, it is possible to achieve a match between human and technological needs. From an examination of the impact of computer based systems on people and their work the book explores the implications of new technology for management and organisations. Analysis of the case studies suggests that new technology may call for new forms of management and organisation if we are to maintain the involvement of people in a technological age.

In an increasingly competitive business environment the book examines the opportunities that combining computer based systems with the effective involvement of people can present to management in improving their effectiveness in terms of quality, customer service and cost effectiveness.

The book demonstrates the relationship between changing technology and corporate culture and how the effective management of change can provide a strategic advantage.

Structure of the Book

In the first part of the book attention is drawn to the increasing recognition that we are not always getting the full benefits from computer technology. There is a general consensus that this is not so much due to the technology itself as to the way it is introduced. Technical decisions at the introductory stage often means that important managerial, organisational and human factors are overlooked and there is a need to adopt a holistic approach to the design and implementation of these new systems.

Previous attempts to combine people and technology have often failed because of the negative effects on the motivation and satisfaction of the people concerned. The book therefore examines what we know about job design and the development of work systems that combine the potential of both people and technology.

Finally in this part of the book the effects of computer technology on people and their jobs are examined and in what is essentially a socio-technical system the potential contribution that job design can make to its effective introduction is explored.

The second part of the book presents a view of what can be achieved in practice in terms of human involvement in technology and its introduction. From the detailed analysis of a case study of a flexible manufacturing system in a small market town it is possible to demonstrate how, by adopting a different approach to the organisation of people and work, high levels of both job satisfaction and performance and of productivity and customer service can be achieved. Similarly, a further example, in terms of the introduction of automated loom building, shows the value of participation in job and systems design.

In the third part of the book some of the problems that arise from the introduction of new systems are explored. The introduction of an automated paint spraying plant in a small engineering company led to many problems, not only of motivation and job satisfaction, but also in terms of the technology and working conditions concerned. Here, problems of linking the new systems to the strategic development of the firm and the failure to consider job design aspects meant that the system was far less flexible in practice than had been planned. Similarly, while computerisation of an order office in a brewery helped to keep costs down, communication and integration between departments deteriorated with negative effects on customer service. In both instances, had socio-technical perspectives been adopted from the start, a very different solution could have transpired.

From these case studies the book explores the implications of new technology for management and organisation. Does not group technology require group forms of organisation, for example? How adequate are existing models of management and organisation and does not new technology require new forms of management and organisation of people and work?

The fourth part of the book examines the relationship between corporate culture and technological change. An example is provided of a large company in the communications business who, in attempting to create a more customer-orientated culture, developed a new computerised customer services system. However, they recognised the need for change, not only in the technology but also in the structure of the organisation and in the jobs and attitudes of staff. Through the use of job design concepts and participative strategies for change, a technology-orientated, bureaucratic system has been transformed into a more people-centred and customer-orientated approach.

However, the ultimate example of putting people first is provided by a case study of a company in the electronics industry who set out to develop a different way of working from the start. This case, which demonstrates the value of the green field site in terms of innovation, provides an example of the strategic advantage of a corporate culture that puts people before technology. Here, with the use of self-managing teams and an emphasis on leadership rather than management from above, high levels of motivation and employee involvement are being achieved. In this environment technological change and people's involvement in the process are taken for granted as part of the continuous process of improvement and increasing organisational effectiveness.

In conclusion the implications of job design for new technology and of new technology for job design are discussed. Whereas the book starts at the level of the individual and his/her job, it concludes at the level of the organisation, its strategy and its culture. It demonstrates the contributions that job design and socio-technical systems thinking can make to the introduction of new technology and how new technology may need new forms of management and organisation,

The book also considers the role that new technology can play in integrating employment conditions and in achieving integration between what have often been functionally separate and independent departments. It considers the role of technologists as agents of change and the opportunities that this creates for a participative approach to job and system design. It emphasises the importance of linking developments in terms of new technology with the strategic objectives of the organisation. Finally, the book examines the role of corporate culture in facilitating this type of change and how new technology can itself act as a catalyst for cultural change.

In conclusion a model is presented showing the factors that influence the effective introduction of new technology and their inter-relationships and how this can inform management in developing a strategy for technological change.

ACKNOWLEDGEMENTS

Many people have given me the information, inspiration and encouragement to write this book.

First and foremost must come the many people from industry and the organisations I visited to conduct my research. These included people from the shop and office floor, trade union representatives, specialists, supervisors, managers and directors and consultants, all of whom gave of their time and interest in discussing the issues concerned. Without their willingness and openness this type of book could never be written and the ideas and information never shared.

Secondly, I would like to thank the people who helped and advised me about the research. In particular I would like to thank the late Jenny Blake of Tavistock Institute who shared my interests in job design and encouraged me to look at the effect of new technology on people and their jobs. Diana Pheysey of Aston University was particularly helpful to me in formulating my initial ideas, but Geoffrey Hutton of Bath University gave me the encouragement and inspiration to see it through.

I also owe a big debt of gratitude to my friends and colleagues in the Polytechnic at Bristol, now the University of the West of England, many of whom have been genuinely interested in the issues and the results of my investigations.

Thanks must also go to such organisations as the Work Research Unit, International Institute of Scientific Management and my many friends and colleagues from the international community through whom I have been able to share my ideas and publish the results of my research.

Finally, my thanks must go to those who have helped me with the publication of this book. In particular John Cushion of Pitmans whose encouragement and genuine interest in the subject has stimulated and motivated me through the different stages of the production. Last and not least my thanks to Barbara Gibbons who, with help from Peter Rogers, has produced the many different drafts required to bring the text and illustrations to the completion stage. Their patience and dedication has finally been rewarded.

PART 1

PEOPLE AND TECHNOLOGY

I   MANAGING TECHNOLOGICAL CHANGE - THE ISSUES

In recent times there is an increasing recognition of the fact that we are often not getting the anticipated benefits from technology. In one study, out of 2000 applications of computers, 40% did not realise their anticipated benefits and of these only 10% were due to technical failure (Long R J 1987). Recognition of the need to examine the management, organisational and human factors associated with technological change is now widespread. In examining some of the most recent literature these findings are, if anything, further reinforced.

In a paper for the Work Research Unit entitled 'Managing corporate change - how to get the best from IT' (Howarth C 1992) the author confirms that organisations are not getting what they expect from technology. However, the problems, she suggests, do not lie with the technology but the way the change is managed. Managing technically linked change calls for total integration of the human, organisational and technical elements of the change throughout the project. In practice the emphasis tends to be on the technology. The neglected factors she suggests sound familiar and include:

- the business circumstances of the organisation
- overall strategic plan
- organisation structure
- existing procedures, practices and systems
- design of jobs
- skills of managers, specialists, clerical and shop floor employees and plans for training and development
- attitudes, motivation and commitment of all employees
- culture of the company
- nature of process of developing and updating technology and extent to which future users are involved

- design methodologies and project management
- composition and effectiveness of any project team
- relationship with suppliers
- state of industrial relations

Recognition of these factors enables an organisation to develop an effective strategy for implementing IT.

This need to take a holistic and integrated approach is also reinforced by (Checkland 1990) and his soft systems methodology. This approach, which recognises the organisation as an open social system, places emphasis on the role played by people and the organisation and the need for integration between its subsystems. His methodology helps those involved distinguish between the problems (expressed in terms of the real world), the development of a model of the activities needed to make the systems work (expressed in conceptual terms) and the use of the model to plan changes for improvement (in the real world). This process, which is essentially cyclical, can, he argues, become a learning process and is in effect an approach to 'continuous improvement'.

Preece, in his excellent book on managing the adoption of new technology (Preece D A 1989), argues that in order to understand what has happened and what is currently happening, it is necessary to employ a broadly based approach, which takes into account objectives, strategies, social processes, organisational structures, infrastructural changes, job design and working practices as well as the technological changes themselves.

In their book on information technology and people (Blackler and Osborne D 1987) contrast what they term the task and technology approach to technical change within an organisation and the end user centred approach. While they acknowledge that the former may be appropriate in some circumstances, eg when it is a straightforward application to existing practices, the intrinsic involvement of end users in the process does offer distinct advantages. They recognise that resistance to change can occur when established practices and methods are threatened and that the approach to organisation developed before IT may need to be discarded. They argue that a pluralist orientation to technical development is required and that the long term issue is not how fast can British work organisations automate, but how can they automate well?

In looking at the development of factory automation systems, FAS, they note that 90-95% of the time is spent on technical aspects and recommend what they define as a parallel approach considering both management and technical aspects together.

These findings are also reinforced by R J Long (1987) in his book on new office information technology. He also contrasts the technical v. user orientated approaches and what he describes as the status quo where no change to the current structure of work is planned.

However, to maximise the potential of new technology he argues that some kind of management approach which can anticipate and deal effectively with the many technological, human resources and strategic issues is necessary. The evidence, he argues, is clear that most office system failures stem from human and managerial problems, not technical factors. This therefore implies that top management must take charge of the process and that there is extensive involvement from both personnel/ human resource departments and computer/information departments. Both have to adopt a different role, with personnel becoming more practical and information department more user orientated.

Rowe's analysis of the problem in terms of optimistic and pessimistic people and chips (Rowe C 1990) continues to be very relevant. The issue is perhaps not whether the technoogy is necessarily good and beneficial and its effect particularly on people inevitably negative and bad, but the fact that we have choices that can be made in the particular and different situations in which it is applied. In making these choices the optimistic and pessimistic perspectives need to be taken into account in order to arrive at a solution that meets the needs and expectations of all those involved.

In their book 'Managing Technology for Competitive Advantage' (Twiss B and Goodridge M 1989) the authors refer to the fact that success in the adoption of new technology is dependent not only on the management of the change in the technology itself but also on the necessary complementary changes to exploit it. It is these technology induced organisational changes that management often have the greatest difficulties with. These frequently involve the culture of the business, its strategies, the organisational structure, managerial attitudes and personnel policies. All elements are interlinked and, like a chain, failure will ensue if one of the links is ineffective.

It is our ability to use technology that distinguishes us from other animals, but this very fact can create resistance and fear of the unhuman. The inability of individuals and organisations to adapt and to utilise the potential of the technological can lead to their demise.

All technology when applied tends to change an organisation and if the introduction is left purely to technologists, these changes are likely to be unforeseen, unplanned and disruptive. Also there is no guarantee that the proposed technology will be appropriate to the needs of the firm. To avoid this 'technology push' situation we need to ensure that the technology is developed in response to the strategic needs and objectives of the firm, ie a 'strategy pull' situation which requires that technologists adopt a more corporate and business orientated role.

However, even the successful adoption will only occur if the change and implementation are managed effectively. Often an attempt to improve the technology fails because the culture, structure, skills and attitudes have evolved to meet different requirements. While it is possible to adapt the technology the organisation needs to change if it is to be successful.

Twiss and Goodridge argue that much can be learnt from the experiences of the relatively few innovative firms which have been outstandingly successful in exploiting new technology. In this respect Zuboff (1992) in her book 'In the Age of the Smart Machine' draws out some of the key characteristics evident in the more innovative firms.

Her comparative studies of the way in which two mills, essentially process industries, adapted to and adopted computer technology revealed a great deal about the culture of the organisation concerned.

In the more innovative organisation, a green field site, operator motivation and commitment was obtained from their involvement in the business and the opportunity to learn and experiment. There was a change both in the nature of the work (from manual to discretionary) and in the style of management and nature of authority. The choice is whether to 'automate' or 'informate'. Informating requires a different role for management and their ability both to share knowledge and information and to create a learning environment. This many found very difficult to do even in the new environment in which they were operating. Essentially we are seeing a situation in which change in technology is challenging traditional boundaries between blue and white collar work and between those that 'manage' and those that 'work'. This also creates the need for a structure that emphasises integration rather than division and equality rather than hierarchy.

As one worker put it:

"If you don't let people grow and develop and make more decisions, its a waste of human life - a waste of human potential. If you don't use your knowledge and skill, its a waste of life. Using technology to its full potential means using man to his full potential."

Thus the issue we need to address in this book is how far is it possible to combine the potential of people and computer technology, and what factors need to be taken into account? How far is it possible to create a meaningful role for the people in the system when capitalising on the undoubted benefits that computer technology affords?

2   WORK SYSTEM DESIGN

In this chapter we need to look at some of the issues involved in the design
of work systems and whether it is possible to design work systems that
combine the potential of both people and technology.

In particular we need to look at what can be learnt from earlier approaches
to industrial organisation and what we know about human needs and
motivation at work.

What should we be trying to achieve in the design of individual's jobs and
how far can alternative forms of work organisation help us to achieve these
objectives?

In particular we need to examine the impact of computer technology on
people and their work and the possible contribution that job design and
work organisation can make to its effective introduction.

2.1 Traditional approaches to work system design

The traditional approach to improving industrial organisation and
efficiency has been based on the dual principles of specialisation of tasks
and centralisation of control and decision making. These principles which
stem from the 'scientific management' approach advocated by F W Taylor
(1947) and the industrial engineering tradition and from classical
organisation theory such as L Urwick and E F L Brech die very hard and
are still evident in a great many organisations today. While they may have
been appropriate in the stable and more predictable environment at the
time, it is very doubtful if this approach achieves the sort of flexibility
required to meet today's changing circumstances.

However, apart from this, the question is how effective this approach has proved in terms of the motivation and satisfaction of the staff concerned. There is much evidence to suggest that the very limited jobs, in terms of the scope of the task and sense of responsibility experienced, results not only in a lack of job satisfaction but poor performance, quality and service to the customer (J Bailey 1983). It also implies that it is management's job to manage and to make the necessary decisions and solve any problems associated with the work. This, apart from adding to costs through increased overheads helps to reinforce the hierarchy and the degree of alienation between management and employees.

2.2 Effects of mechanisation

Add to this situation the effects of mechanisation and we can begin to see how the combined results of management strategies and technology can undermine people and their ability to contribute to what the organisation is trying to achieve.

Of course the classic illustration of the negative effects of technology is the picture of 'man on the assembly line' (Beynon 1973). In many senses this epitomises all the worst features of mechanisation and what Davis (1978) describes as technological determinism. Here people performing what are often the most minimal of tasks are divorced from their colleagues by the length of the line, divorced from the product and seeing the job through to completion. Their work is paced by the speed of the line which is effectively controlled by management.

Thus, as previous research has indicated (Blauner 1964) the individual is alienated not only from management and those that make the decisions, but also from the process and the job itself. It often means that the only sense of satisfaction for people in such circumstances is the pay packet at the end of the week or the disruption that they can cause to the system to which they have been subjected.

Of course no one could deny the enormous benefits in terms of improved productivity that the application of technology brings, but if the approach adopted results in the alienation of the people concerned its full benefits will not be obtained. The results of this approach not only in terms of bad industrial relations, stoppages and strikes are only too well known but also increasing competition has helped management to recognise its costs in terms of poor performance, quality and service to the customer.

2.3 What do people look for from their work?

Recognition of the problems created by the scientific management approach to organisation was recognised as far back as the 1930's with the Hawthorne studies which drew attention to the importance of human and social factors at work and their effects on attitudes and output. However social psychologists such as D McGregor (1960), A M Maslow (1943) and F Herzberg (1966) have drawn our attention to people's needs for psychological fulfilment from their work and the importance of such things as variety, job interest, responsibility, recognition, sense of achievement and the opportunity to develop new skills in motivating people to the task. In fact writers such as Argyris (1964) have suggested that the strikes and wage claims experienced by management in the past were a reaction from employers to their experience of work and were their way of compensating for it. People like McGregor suggested in his theory that if you treat people like children they will behave like children, but that given trust and responsibility the majority of employees will respond in a particular way and substantiate management faith in them. Maslow suggested that while the majority of employees may have satisfied their basic psychological and social needs few, only perhaps 10%, felt psychologically fulfilled.

2.4 Work restructuring

It was this realisation of the untapped potential in the workforce that led to earlier attempts to improve motivation though the redesign of jobs and restructuring of work.

The earlier experiments by organisations such as Philips in job rotation and job enlargement showed what could be achieved in terms of improved productivity and job satisfaction (Buchanan D A 1979). However, while very beneficial in increasing the scope of the task, job interest, variety and social contact, this approach is criticised for its lack in delegating real responsibility. Job enrichment on the other hand implies the delegation of responsibility for decisions relating to planning, organisation and control in relation to the tasks and has far wider implications for change in the structure and style of management in the organisation. Nevertheless considerable benefits in terms of improved motivation were achieved as a result of job enrichment in organisations such as ICI at the time (Paul W J and Robertson K B 1970).

2.5 Job design

The success of the earlier work restructuring experiments has led to the recognition of the importance of good job design and the development of the criteria and type of job characteristics that one should be trying to build into people's work.

For example the Tavistock Institute in particular has done a great deal to help identify principles that should be applied to the design of the job at the level of the individual (Emery F E and Thorsrud F 1969).

These include the individual's ability to make a recognisable contribution to the product and to obtain feedback on quantity and quality. They should also be able to undertake a meaningful 'whole' task, to have the opportunity to make decisions relating to the work and to experience a variety of tasks within an optimum cycle time (see Figure 2.1).

Figure 2.1   Principles of Job Design - Tavistock Institute Model

Individual jobs should provide:

- variety
- a meaningful task
- optimum work cycle
- control over work standards and feedback of results
- preparation and auxiliary tasks
- use of valued skill and knowledge
- contribution to end product

More recently J R Hackman and G Oldham (1980) developed an operational model that identified the core job characteristics or dimensions that we should be trying to achieve. The model links job characteristics with the desired psychological state of the individual and the outcomes in terms of motivation and job performance (see Figure 2.2)

The model, which incorporates the need to recognise individual differences, provides the basis for analysing and diagnosing motivational problems at work. However it can also be used to anticipate the effects of changes eg in terms of technology on people's jobs and to help plan new work systems.

Thus in terms of job design we have the means and the opportunity to design jobs that are both meaningful and motivational. The question is whether these opportunities are recognised and if so whether they are taken?

Figure 2.2   Operational Model of Job Design

The full model: how use of the implementing concepts can lead to positive outcomes

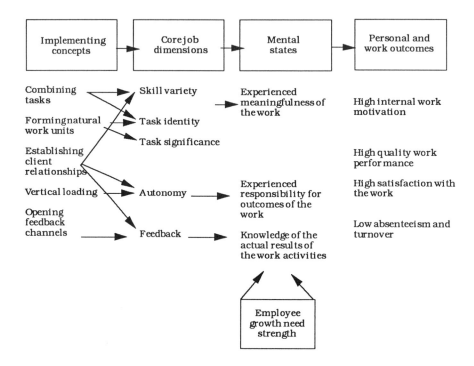

2.6 Groups forms of work organisation

Reference has been made to the suggested limitations of previous approaches to job design. For example critics would argue that job rotation only moved people from one meaningless job to another and job enlargement does not involve any increase in real responsibility.

Job enrichment, while good in theory, is difficult to apply on an individual basis because, with the exception of people such as sales personnel, few people work in isolation and therefore it is not possible to make changes to one person's job without making changes to the group as a whole.

Consequently people came to recognise the relevance of group working as a means not only of achieving increased social interaction and satisfaction but also because of the opportunities it affords for job rotation, job enlargement and job enrichment.

In many circumstances necessity forces the issue when for example companies begin to develop Group Technology as a more flexible and versatile work system. This form of work organisation requires more flexible and versatile people to work in it. As one Japanese manager put it 'group technology requires group forms of work organisation'.

Thus the concept of the autonomous or semi-autonomous group found considerable favour not only with manufacturing industry but also within commerce, service industries and the public sector. The work of people such as R Wild and D Birchall (1975) highlighted the extent of its application and the elements and aspects of decision making that were increasingly being delegated to such work groups.

2.7 Socio-technical systems design

As we discussed in the previous chapter the introduction of new technology in the form of computer systems of manufacture or information can have a significant and substantial effect on the organisation, not only in changes in technology but in its impact on people and their jobs and on the social structure of the organisation including communications, relationships and decision making.

Whether this impact is positive or negative on the people concerned is very much influenced by the way the system is introduced and the attitudes and interests of those involved.

From an early stage the Tavistock Institute identified the importance of reorganising an organisation as a socio-technical system in which changes to one system, namely the technology, were likely to have a significant impact on the other, the social structure. Their work in the Durham Coal Mines revealed the effects that mechanisation in the coal mines had on the jobs of the coal miners and on the social structure concerned (Trist and Bamforth 1951). They recognised that it was not necessary to bow to the inevitability of 'technological determinism' and that it is possible to exercise 'organisation choice' in designing a work system that fulfils both the human and social needs as well as the technical and economic requirements of the organisation.

The classic example of these developments has been the experiences of Volvo particularly in their plant at Kalmar. Here they abolished the assembly line and created a new factory concept where small groups take complete responsibility for a major stage of vehicle manufacture. Aided by their own computer terminals the work groups are able to manage their own performance, work in progress and inventory. While more costly in initial terms, the benefits in improved quality, motivation, labour turnover and industrial relations, they feel, have more than repaid the investment incurred.

Volvo's experiences at Kalmar demonstrate that we have choices both in the disposition of the technology and in the social structure. This adds further support to the fact that it is possible to design systems that are efficient and effective in economic, technical and human terms.

2.8 Impact of computer systems on people's jobs

Replicating some earlier research (Davis LE and Taylor JCE 1978) Taylor pointed to the fact that, in both the design of new production facilities and in computer installation, the production engineers and systems analysts have operated from traditional job design criteria, eg specialisation of tasks, minimising skills and training time. As Taylor said 'They still prefer to minimise the immediate costs of production rather than emphasise a longer term approach to give job design which recognises the economic costs of worker frustration and acknowledges employee satisfaction and motivation'.

Research on the impact of computer systems on people's jobs shows that it is not the technology itself but the way it is applied that creates either positive or negative effects on people's jobs, ie technology as such tends to be neutral. Also it is unlikely to be good or bad in all respects. Depending on the application some job characteristics such as task identity and feedback may improve and others such as social interaction may decrease.

In their research Buchanan and Boddy (1983) investigated the impact of computer systems in a number of different organisational applications. In the case of biscuit making, for example, the job of the doughman, which had been a very skilled position making the dough for the rest of the line, had now been automated by the computer. The effect of this had been to remove much of their sense of responsibility and interest, creating a routine repetitive job with comparatively little task identity and social interaction. The author argued that the job could however have been enriched by allowing the operator to operate the new recipe desk but because this would mean cutting across the existing physical layout and organisation structure it was difficult to implement.

This contrasted with the oven man's job which had been enriched by computerisation and thus the operator had a visible goal and retained his discretion and control over the process. He got rapid feedback on performance and felt that the job had more interest and challenge.

The researchers point to the fact that it could have been possible to create a line team but that management's decisions were constrained by the existing technology, physical layout and structural arrangements.

Similarly a study was done on the effects of introducing word processing in a marine engineering consultancy firm. Here the decision to centralise the word processing facilities in order to improve the service and reduce costs resulted in a significant reduction in the job satisfaction of the staff concerned. Not only did factors such as their identity with the tasks and work group decline but also autonomy, variety and feedback were reduced. No actual improvements were achieved in terms of either costs or the service provided. Here the obvious benefits of the computerised system were undermined by the negative effects on the employees concerned as a result of the way the technology was introduced. Concern for the effective use of the equipment and for management control of the process led to the results obtained.

Here again alternative solutions that offered a better fit between the technology and the people concerned were possible; for example, a decentralised system in which the word processors were available to each office and where the typist remained as part of the team could have been more effective.

These examples lend support to the idea that in designing a work system employing computer technology we need to look more widely than the individual tasks to identify all those who need to work together in order to provide the customer with the product or service that they require. This group or team of people can form the basis of an efficient and effective work system with which the individuals concerned can identify.

Conclusions to Part I

In the first part of the book we have been looking at the overall issues involved in managing people and technological change.

There is, as we discussed, quite widespread recognition of the fact that we are often not gaining full advantage of the new computer technology. This as several authors have identified is not so much a problem of the technology itself as the way it is introduced. The technical dominance in the introductory stage often means that important management organisational and human factors are overlooked. They argue that it is important to take a holistic approach and that these social factors as well as the technology are taken into account at the design stage.

Examination of earlier attempts to combine people and technology suggests that it was the negative effects of specialisation and centralised control that resulted in the problems of motivation, morale, quality and performance. The resultant research led to experiments in alternative forms of work organisation and in identification of what we should be trying to achieve in terms of job design.

Whilst it appears that we have been slow to learn from these lessons more recent research into the impact of computer technology suggests that these options and alternatives are equally applicable to the current situation. The tools and techniques of job design can be used to help us design an efficient and effective work system that combines the needs of both the people and the technology.

The question is whether the need and opportunity for job design is recognised and how it can be applied in practice. These aspects will be examined through a practical investigation of the first two major case studies of computer application which form the second part of the book.

PART II

OPPORTUNITIES CREATED BY
TECHNOLOGICAL CHANGE

3 MATCHING PEOPLE AND TECHNOLOGY - A CASE STUDY OF FLEXIBLE MANUFACTURING

3.1 The factory of the future

The next major question we need to address is how far in practice is it possible to match people's needs with those of the computer and new technology? How far can human factors be taken into account in the design of computer automated systems of information and manufacture, without jeopardising the technical integrity and economic effectiveness of these systems?

Some useful insights to this question come from the first major case study on the introduction of a flexible manufacturing system in a large engineering firm. The opportunity to study this came as a result of following up an article in the New Scientist (March 1981) which, in describing the FMS, spoke of 'the factory of the future'. However, since reference was also made to the use of teamwork, it seemed to be a promising situation for further investigation. The opportunity was taken to arrange a visit for a group of management students who were studying job design. From our initial impressions, it appeared that a small group of employees, with a minimum of management interference, were able to run a factory producing complex products, utilising advanced computer controlled equipment, with both high levels of satisfaction and interest, and of output and productivity.

Following negotiations with the Manufacturing Director, it proved possible to gain further access to study the situation in more detail. While it would be useful to examine the performance of the system, it would be particularly interesting to explore the approach adopted to work organisation and job design, and also to the management of the system. How had they been able to introduce such radical changes and how genuine was the apparent commitment and involvement of the workforce?

To help plan the approach to collecting data a questionnaire was prepared (see Appendix 1), which highlighted a number of the key aspects involved in introducing new technology. This served as a guide to planning interviews and for subsequent analysis. The questionnaire was based on a broad model of socio-technical systems identifying some of the key variables involved (see Appendix 2)

In order to explore these issues, interviews were arranged with the Manufacturing Director who had been instrumental in introducing these changes, with the Factory Manager who was responsible for the plant, with the Trade Union Convenor who had been involved in the negotiations for the plant and with the 11 staff who were working in the new factory. It was decided to utilise more objective measures to assess the changes in job content and satisfaction by employing the job diagnostic survey developed by Hackman and Oldham (1980). This, when used together with follow-up small group discussions, provided some valuable comparative data on peoples' opinions about their jobs before and after the introduction of the new system.

The results of these investigations were presented in a paper to an international conference in Helsinki (Bailey J 1984). The conference was on 'Organisation and New Technology' and the paper entitled 'Matching People and Technology' forms the basis of the case study which follows. It was in many senses an eye opener and a vision of what the factory of the future could be. It seemed so revolutionary to find such a small, quiet, clean factory working so unobtrusively in a small industrial estate in a country market town and yet achieving remarkable levels of output, productivity, lead times and delivery dates. Yet all this was being achieved with a minimal sized workforce who, nevertheless, had a very high level of involvement and satisfaction with their working conditions.

3.2 The problems of small batch production

One of the biggest problems facing companies in the engineering industry is how to achieve efficiency and high productivity in small batch operations. In mass production, considerable savings are possible through mechanisation   because of the long runs of standardised products. However, 75% of the engineering industry is engaged in manufacture of batch quantities of less than 50 components and, until computerisation, it has not been possible to utilise the advantage in these circumstances.

A further problem, apart from the relatively high costs of small batch production, is that of delivery dates where, because of the time it takes to set up a machine, the only economical way is to produce a complete batch of each part in turn. This means that the final product can only be assembled when all the parts have been machined which can take several months and it only takes a problem of scrap on one batch of a particular component to hold the whole job up.

A further factor in this approach to small batch production is the very high costs of inventory and work in progress that is built up especially when a wider variety of products are being handled in the system at the same time. This, added to the complexities and costs of production control in these circumstances, leads to a very inefficient and costly production system.

3.3 An alternative approach to production organisation

In order to counteract these problems the firm, a large, essentially mechanical engineering company involved in high technology products for defence and commercial applications, had recently introduced a flexible manufacturing system in one of its divisions.

Taking the opportunity presented by a large new defence contract, it was decided to create a manufacturing cell employing the latest in computer aided manufacturing techniques. The aim was to reduce work in progress, to eliminate non-production time and to achieve shorter lead times and delivery dates. This would be achieved by manufacturing components based on families rather than batches and using computers for loading and controlling the machining process and for scheduling and production control.

In addition, it was recognised that to achieve full benefit from the new production system a different style of working would be required from the workforce than in a conventional machine shop. Thus, from the outset it was made clear that employees working with the new system would have to be flexible and prepared to work as a team, going where the work demanded rather than remaining on one particular machine.

3.4 The technical system

The new system took between 12/18 months to develop around

machines which were readily available commercially and were already in use in the main factory. A small team of production and software engineers aided by University staff and research students developed the new system based on two very large KTM machining centres. These machines, which are capable of drilling and milling a wide range of components, are linked directly to the factory's main computer which supplies instructions about how to mill and drill the parts and what tools are required for the operations. The machine can choose from 40 tools stored in a carousel and a mechanical arm picks up the right tool and inserts it into the machine chuck. A further 80 tools are stored in an ancillary rack and a mechanical arm transfers the required tools to the carousel, from which it is transferred to the chuck.

A further development is the automation of the loading of the machines. A mobile trolley incorporating a robot, was specially designed which automatically selects and loads the required pallet on to the machine which then holds the part for machining. Apart from removing the heavy physical work involved and the element of risk to safety, it also saves time by allowing the operator to continue working on other parts.

The essential feature therefore in the new machinery process is that the machining centres are, in effect, versatile machines equally capable of milling, drilling, turning or grinding as opposed to conventional dedicated machinery, eg lathes or milling machines. These machines, coupled to computer control, are able to reload and program themselves to machine all the parts required for a component in sequence, rather than in batches. This enables the system to produce all the parts required to assemble the first complete unit rather than having to wait for all the batches to be complete.

The factory was designed as a versatile system and can manufacture a range of products from the engine for a microlight aircraft, to a current complex mechanism used in the aircraft industry. This mechanism involves some 100 different piece parts, of which only a relatively small proportion are completed on the machining centres. However, these are the most complicated parts to machine and represent the majority of the total costs. The remaining parts are either bought in or machined on the conventional and numerically controlled machines that make up the rest of the machining capacity of the cell.

Finally, as can be seen from the Figure 3.1, the cell also includes its own heat treatment, crack detection, plating, assembly and test area and is therefore a totally self-contained manufacturing unit.

Whilst being advanced technically the new system also provided very different working conditions from a human point of view to a conventional factory. It was a small factory unit, in a separate building on a trading estate in a small country market town. The conditions were, by contrast to the main factory, very clean, light and quieter and provided a much more pleasant and intimate environment to work in. We were very struck by this example of what the factory of the future could look and feel like for those working there.

Figure 3.1 Layout of flexible manufacturing system

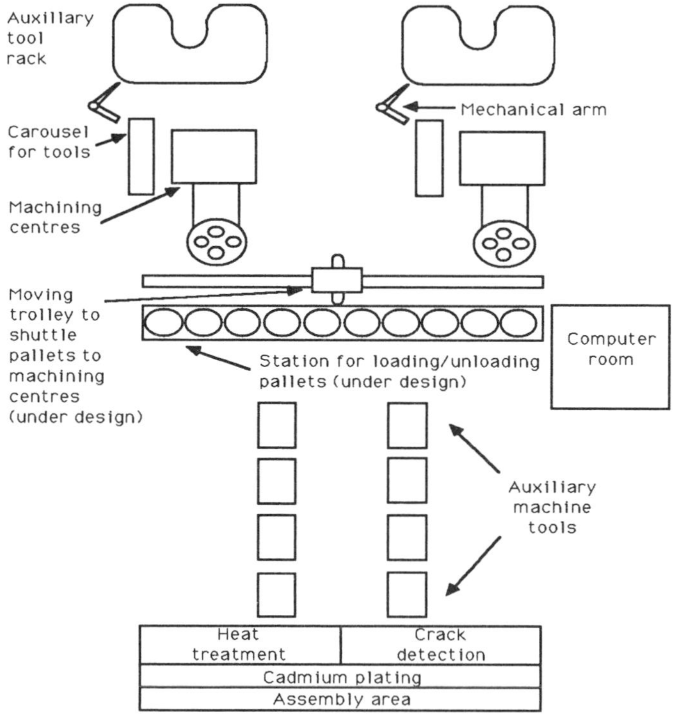

3.5 Job design and work organisation

Apart from the new technology what is of particular interest is the approach adopted to work organisation and how this has affected the design and content of individual jobs. In order to avoid any waiting through all machines not working all the time, staff who applied to work were advised that they would have to be prepared to work on a flexible basis and as a team. Thus, it would be up to them to go where the work demanded, whether this was on the machining centres, conventional machines, plating or finishing operations, including assembly of the final component. This was made very clear by the Manufacturing Director, the Site Manager and the Trade Union Convenor.

To examine what effect the form of work organisation adopted had on peoples' sense of satisfaction and involvement, the job diagnostic survey developed by Hackman and Oldham (1980) was used. This involved issuing a questionnaire to the staff involved and holding follow-up discussions in small groups to discuss the results and their reasons for their responses.

The questionnaire taps people's reactions to their jobs and to such characteristics as variety, autonomy, task identity and feedback in particular. These factors which are based on extensive research into motivation and job design are considered to be key factors relating to job satisfaction (Hackman J R and Oldham G, 1980).

The approach adopted to work organisation meant that in contrast to a conventional machine shop organisation where people could be stuck on one batch of components on one machine, here people experience a very large degree of variety in their work. Another key difference is in their sense of identity with the task. In a conventional shop people said that they did not really know what the component was that they were machining, what it was for or where it went when they had finished it. Here however, with it being a small unit, organised on the basis of group technology, it was possible not only to see the finished product but also be involved in most of the stages of its manufacture, including quite frequently assisting in its final assembly. This appears to provide people with a high level of task identity and was frequently quoted as being a major source of job satisfaction. However, while many people felt that the computer had detracted from their job in terms of the skill and discretion that they could employ in the machining process, this had, to a consider-able extent, been compensated by the discretion that they could exercise regarding the organisation of the work. As one person said "the first thing I do when I come on the shift is to see where the work is" and with the style of management adopted, the work group and individuals are given a high degree of responsibility to decide on which job or machines to work.

Whilst there has been no significant change in the degree of feedback they get from the job itself, their feelings are that the significance of their work has been enhanced by the new arrangements. A summary of the reactions of the employees in the unit to their jobs is shown in the Figure 3.2, which analyses the extent to which desirable motivational job characteristics are present in that situation. While further comparative research would be necessary, there does appear to be some evidence that the choices made regarding the form of work organisation used have been a significant factor in influencing employees' reaction to their new job and to the technical system adopted.

Figure 3.2   Reactions to job characteristics

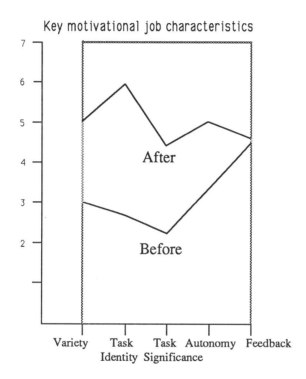

Key motivational job characteristics

3.6 Organisation structure and management style

There are also significant differences in terms of the structure of the organisation and the style of management employed which appear to affect the motivation and sense of involvement of the work force. Because the computer is able to tackle a number of the administrative jobs associated with the production process, the factory runs with very slim management and administrative overheads. Scheduling of work and the progress functions are performed by the computer so that the factory manager is able to tell at any time exactly who is working on what and what stage of progress the job has reached. This removes the necessity for administrative and clerical staff to carry out these functions. Similarly, since the direct machining is computer controlled and the workforce take on a lot of the responsibility for allocating people to the work, there is no necessity for intermediate supervision at chargehand or foreman level. Not only does this mean reductions in overheads, it also creates the opportunity for greater involvement by the workforce in what have traditionally been management prerogatives. In particular, despite automation and computerisation, problems do occur in the production process and the manager concerned invites a high degree of involvement from the workforce in tackling problems on the shop floor and in reviewing progress and performance.

The size of the unit, with a total staff of only 12, is felt by most people to be a very significant factor in creating the sense of involvement and team working that is evident in the factory. While people miss to some extent the contact with a wider group of people, they argue that in a smaller unit you cannot afford to get at cross purposes with the other people and that they have got to make it work.

It was quoted that decentralisation and the creation of a smaller unit was one of the advantages arising from the computer and new technology. It was felt that the new system provides autonomy not only at shop floor level but also to an increasing degree for local management. While the factory manager's job might involve a wider range of activities and functions than would normally be the case, there was also some scope for flexibility and choice in the way that the operation was managed.

3.7 Introduction of change

Of particular significance in aiding the introduction of new technology in this company was the market situation and the industrial relations climate within the firm. The company, which is relatively young in its attitudes and age structure, appears to have developed a very good working relationship with the trade unions who have accepted the need for change. Although there is no comprehensive 'New Technology Agreement' as such, the unions have accepted that the use of new technology is vital to the firm's survival and are prepared to work with the company over its introduction. In respect of the FMS system, advanced warning and consultation with the unions took place at least 12 months in advance and because of demand for its products the firm was able to guarantee that no redundancies would occur as a result of its introduction.

Staff for the new factory were recruited internally on the basis of volunteers. The unions had accepted that the new system would require changed work practice and it was a classic example of a fully flexible cell manufacturing approach. It demanded, in the unions opinion, a high degree of flexibility, co-operation and team work and, while there was less use of individual skills, the jobs were more interesting. The trade unions agreed with the company that this was the way to go.

In practice, it has tended to be the younger, more highly trained employees who have transferred to the new factory and who have found the computerised equipment and new style of working more easy to accept. Most of them are skilled craftsmen having served a Company Apprenticeship. Whilst a number moved initially for domestic reasons, many were attracted by the opportunity to learn new skills and be involved in the development of 'the factory of the future'. While many had severe reservations and anxieties about the change, only one person asked to be transferred back and the manager has said that the majority would not wish to return to the old methods, which was confirmed by the workforce.

The timescale for this type of development is quite long in that it has taken more than two years to get the system fully developed. But in the company's experience it has been system problems and programming the machines successfully which have presented the major hurdles to overcome. Possibly, because of this, the emphasis in terms of involvement in the planning process has come from the technical functions. The project team planning the change and new system primarily comprised production engineers and software specialists with external help from a local University under the chairmanship of the Manufacturing Director. There was no direct involvement by unions or shop floor, or for that matter by other functions such as personnel or industrial relations, or from the design side.

3.8 Results and benefits
To an outside observer the results and benefits of the new system have been very impressive. Although the company was reluctant to disclose financial information, the result of the new systems can be summarised

as follows:

i. The throughput, or lead time, for completion of products has been reduced. In the case of the current component, lead time using conventional techniques would have been 4/6 months and this has been reduced to 14 days.

ii. Work in progress and inventory costs have been substantially reduced.

iii. The system is more cost effective than a traditional factory.

iv. The system saves substantially on set-up times and as a result of the reliability of the equipment and planned maintenance the factory achieves a very high 'up running' time for the engineering industry.

v. The jobs in the system appear more satisfying than in a conventional machine shop and this appears to improve the motivation of the staff concerned.

vi. The form of work organisation chosen has enhanced co-operation and the feeling of team work. People more readily identify with the overall performance of the factory.

vii. The computerised system and style of management chosen permit a relatively high degree of involvement of the workforce in problem solving and managing the operation.

3.9 Questions arising from the case study

The following questions can be considered either by individual readers and students or as a basis for group discussion and case study work:

1. What were the primary factors which led the company into making these changes?

2. From where did the initiative for making the change come? What was involved in the process and what influence did they have on the results?

3. What factors were considered to be important in staffing the new system and how did these influence the form of work organisation that was adopted.

4. What were the critical features of the organisation of the new system adopted and how did these affect the nature and design of people's jobs, their motivation and satisfaction?

5. Do you feel the company was successful in combining human and technological needs? Give reasons for your answer.

6. Does the case provide any insights about changes in the nature of the   management role in these situations?

3.10 Observations and analysis of FMS case

While many specific points have arisen from the description of the flexible manufacturing systems case, a number of more general observations can be made about it as an illustration of what is possible in terms of job and work organisation design in the introduction of new technology.

❑ **Business and manufacturing strategy**

Comments were made in the case study about the changing environment in which manufacturing industry finds itself today.   In many industries apart from engineering, an organisation's competitive position depends not only on factors such as price, but increasingly on factors such as quality, consumer choice, product design and diversity, speed of delivery and back-up service. These criteria, rather than being based on efficiency or use alone, put a premium on overall organisational effectiveness and meeting the customer's needs.

To be effective in such a dynamic and diverse environment and market place, pressure is put on the organisation's flexibility and ability to respond to changing customer demands.   Thus, to some extent, if organisation and internal environment mirror the external environment this then gives the company a competitive advantage.

This means that the design of the organisation needs to be seen as a strategic issue central to the effectiveness and survival of the business.

❑ **Technological choice**

The case also provides an illustration of the choices that are possible in the disposition of technology. Until comparatively recently, the assumption was often made that technology is finite and that all the other variables including people and work organisation would fit round the technology. However, developments such as at Volvo and Saab challenged the assumption of 'technological determinism' and demonstrated that options and alternatives were possible which might better fit some of the other variables involved, eg people.

The use of Group Technology in this case is a further example of how the grouping of related machinery and equipment in a family or cell-like situation can, apart from creating considerable operational advantages, now provide a sense of task identity and involvement in the whole process that traditional and functional forms of organisation have found it hard to achieve.

❏ Decentralisation and information control

The use in this case of computerised systems of information and management also demonstrates what is possible in terms of both decentralisation of control but also in the integration of functions and activities. As opposed to large numbers of specialised staff being employed in production control and scheduling, these functions were decentralised to the operational teams of the manager and the work group. This, plus the inherent flexibility of the computer controlled machine, meant that a high level of local autonomy on production, planning and control was possible, considerably aiding the flexibility and responsiveness of the system.

❏ Smaller autonomous units

Turning from technology to the question of organisation structure, the use of a smaller decentralised unit does appear to have significant advantage particularly in regard to communication and the sense of involvement of the workforce in the organisation as a whole. The feature was recognised in the earlier work on socio-technical systems and the opportunities existing for 'organisational choice' (Trist and Bamforth).

This form of decentralisation is made possible by the disposition of the technology and by the computerised information systems. The fact that the unit can have all these facilities and resources required to make a complete product means that it can be both geographically and organisationally relatively independent of other parts of the organisation, whereas with a traditional functional organisation the various specialised departments need to be closely related to facilitate communication and the movement of work. Also the decentralised computer information system means that the majority of management decisions and control can be taken at the base level.

❏ **Teamwork**

Although chosen for primarily operational reasons the decision to adopt a
flexible pattern of working and team work does seem to have influenced
peoples' reaction to their job in a very positive way. Although the
advances in technology may have detracted from their manual skills, a lot
of discretion had been retained regarding the organisation of the work and
this, together with the variety of working at different stages of the
process, helps to achieve a high sense of task identity and involvement in
the total operation. This does suggest that group forms of organisation
may often be more appropriate to computer based systems of manufacture
than traditional forms of work organisation.

❏ **Employee and trade union participation**

Finally, the case does demonstrate the importance of the involvement of
employees and their trade union representatives in the change process. In
this instance the attitudes of the trade unions towards the introduction of
new technology and the changes in work organisation required appeared
to be influenced by their involvement and consultation on the strategic
issues and developments of the firm. It is difficult to see how trade unions
can be expected to accept the extent of changes required by new
technology unless there is involvement at that level. The threat to the
traditional role of trade unions of maintaining the employment of craft and
skills of their members means that they can have legitimate and well
founded concern about the introduction of new technology and
management's objectives in doing so. Only very full involvement and
consultation with regard to the objectives of the change and the approach
to its introduction are likely to overcome the natural resistance and fears
that trade unions and their members may feel.

These issues and the question of employee involvement in the
development of their new systems will be more fully illustrated by the next
case study on Automated Loom Building.

Summary

The value of this case therefore is that it shows what is possible in
terms of achieving a satisfactory match between human and technological
needs. To some extent, perhaps unconsciously and largely for
operational rather than social reasons, the case demonstrates that options
and alternatives are possible in the disposition of both the people and
the technology. Combining what was in effect a group form of

organisation with a group form of technology enabled people to feel involved and responsible despite the advanced levels of automation concerned.

While this case has demonstrated a number of positive factors that can help to achieve this result, it still leaves the question as to why, in other situations and applications, similar results are not obtained. Analysis of the subsequent cases in Part III will help to answer this question.

4   AUTOMATED LOOM BUILDING - PARTICIPATION IN JOB AND SYSTEM DESIGN

4.1 Background to the company and case study

The value of participation and the involvement of all parties in the process of job and system design is evident from the next case study on the introduction of automated loom building in a large aircraft manufacturer.

The Research and Technology Division, while heavily involved in developments in design and manufacturing technology, had recognised that changes in these aspects had important human and organisational consequences. Indeed, their objective (raison d'etre) was defined as the promotion of technological and organisational *change* within the group.

The company, which at the time employed over 10,000 people at three different sites, had had an interest in employee involvement for some time. Trade Union consultation took place through a highly influential committee and an Employee Involvement Department which was headed by an ex-convenor of thefactory and was quite separate from the Personnel Department.

The Research and Technology Division, which researched optimal manufacturing techniques, systems and operational structures for all parts of the group, sought to work in an interactive way involving all parties at all levels in the process of change. Having identified an opportunity for the use of new technology, they then researched and demonstrated this to potential users. The demonstration provided the opportunity to involve the potential user and gain their commitment to its development. Therefore, their intention was for the user to take up the process of development with R & T in a supportive role.

Whilst R & T start their projects from a technological base, they seek early recognition of the opportunities for systems integration and organisational benefits. Thus, it was recognised in R & T that most projects have technological and organisational implications both horizontally and vertically and depend for their success on how much people can work together. However, it is perhaps important to note that while this fact was clearly recognised, it did not appear to be reflected in the allocation and distribution of their resources. All the staff involved were technology based and, although they had some awareness of the issues, were not trained in psychology or the behavioural sciences.

This case study is, therefore, interesting on three levels:

❑   Firstly, as an example of technological change and automation in manufacturing and the fact that choices and options are available.

❑   Secondly, as an illustration of participation in job and system design in practice.

❑   Thirdly, as an example of organisation development and the role of technologists in stimulating organisational change.

In terms of the research and data collection, the author's role in this case was one of advisor and observer. Through contacts with the Project Manager access was provided to visit the existing loom factory, study the traditional methods of loom building and talk to the loom builders themselves. Also through involvement with R & T it was possible to obtain technical background information on loom technology and the issues involved in its development.

As a result of these contacts there was an opportunity to follow through the development of the automated approach to loom building. This allowed for visits to the R & T Division to talk to the loom builders involved in the loom building improvements. This they described as 'job design' without really realising that this was an acknowledged discipline.

Unfortunately, although access was sought to conduct more detailed analysis of the changes to the job characteristics as a result of introducing the new technology, this was not possible, due to trade union sensitivity. However, informal discussions provided some useful impressions of their reactions to the proposed system.

Apart from this material for this case study was also drawn from a paper presented at the 1st International Conference on Human Factors in Manufacturing in London (Mills 1984).

4.2 Loom building

Modern aircraft and military versions in particular have a large amount of electrical and electronic equipment for aircraft and weapons control and guidance. The wiring looms which power these various instruments and pieces of equipment are therefore very complicated and this is reflected in the length and complexity of the manufacturing process.

Traditionally, wiring looms have been built manually by skilled electricians assembling the looms on large boards standing vertically, often 15-20 ft (4.5-6m) in length and 10 ft (3m) in height. This is a detailed and laborious task and it can take as much as three to six weeks to assemble some of the more complex looms. Because of the requirement for accuracy and attention to detail the work is self-paced and no bonus schemes operate. The work, though painstaking, appears leisurely but requires considerable skill and patience. With the more complicated looms involving up to 2500 cables of 12 metre lengths, it takes a qualified electrician of average skill up to four years to develop the experience and skill level required to assemble the loom.

The first stage in manufacture is to cut the cables to length in a cutting room largely staffed by semi-skilled female operators. Each cable is then marked with an alpha-numeric identification which is printed on the plastic sleeves which are slipped on to the end of each cable.

The cables are then handed to the loom builder in kit form, together with the fittings required such as pins, terminal plugs and sockets. The operator then assembles the loom on a loom board and working from a drawing forms the cable into bunches, laying individual cables along designated routes, adding and subtracting from the bunches, strapping the wires together, cutting to length, stripping the insulation from the cable ends and crimping the terminals into place.

Further complications arise from the use of some 70 different cable and terminal types, many of which require the use of dedicated hand tools.

The most time-consuming part of the job is the sorting process, identifying

35

cables, sorting them out from a bunch and choosing which cable to break out from the main bunch.

An analysis of the elements of the current manual loom building process and the average amount of time spent on each task is shown in Figure 4.1.

Figure 4.1   Cost breakdown of typical aircraft loom

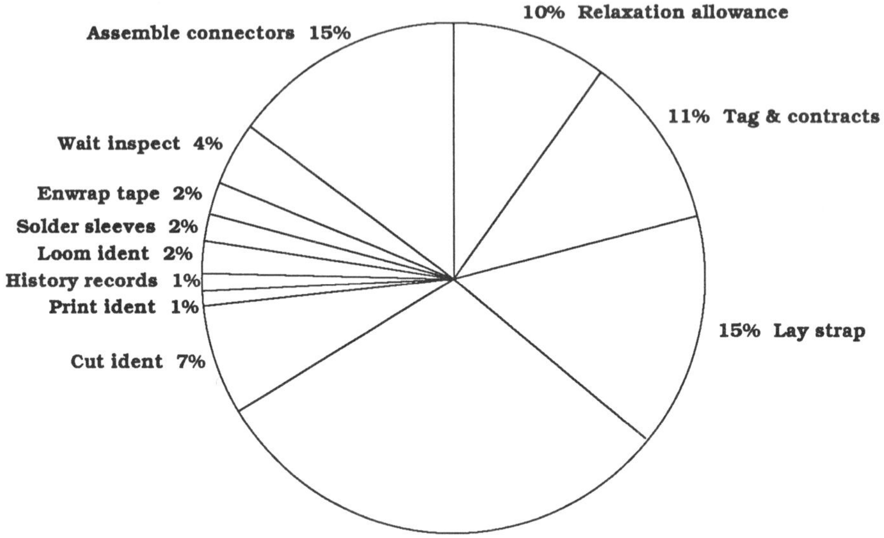

4.3 **The technological menu**

Increasing competition in the aircraft industry led to pressure on costs. Continuing developments in aircraft design involved still greater use of electrical/electronic equipment and increased the importance of loom manufacture. In these circumstances, the cost of loom building assumes greater importance and the company was forced to look at alternative approaches to loom manufacture. Studies of the anticipated future work load for the loom shop showed that a 40% increase in manning levels could be required over a period of six years if the current manufacturing methods were not changed. This knowledge, added to opportunities that were evident from the study of the loom building process, provided the incentives for an investigation by R & T into the potential for mechanisation and automation in the loom building process. This study revealed that while the job was quite skilled and complicated, it comprised a number of discrete operations, many of which were capable of mechanisation.

Following further investigation and desk research, methods of mechanising most of the operations were identified and the investigation stage culminated in the production of a menu of *'candidate'* manufacturing techniques which would then be offered as demonstration of their potential to the user. The demonstration effectively showed the options and alternatives that might be available in terms of loom building technology. Apart from demonstrating individual stand-alone items and pieces of equipment, methods of mechanical handling of the reels and cut lengths of cable were also demonstrated. As a first step they demonstrated schematic alternatives and options as to how these items would be grouped together and the potential or computer control of the process.

Consideration of the staffing of the schematic layouts highlighted a number of important points.

❏ That some tasks arising out of the present loom design could never be mechanised and mechanical methods would always be interspersed by manual tasks.

❏ Different looms required different combinations of technology and therefore an important part of the task of data preparation would be the interpretation of loom design and selection of the appropriate technology and manufacturing process.

❏ Job design and the involvement of the user, ie the loom builders with their experience and knowledge of the process, was as important as the design of the technology.

4.4 Participative job and systems design

The approach adopted to job design in this case needs to be set against the background and culture of the company and its approach to participation and employee involvement. As mentioned earlier, the company had a declared policy of fostering the active participation of managers, trade union representation and all employees. Apart from a joint management and trade union group and company council, the employee involvement department seeks to develop awareness and participation in company issues at all levels.

As the project manager described:

"Over recent years the representatives of bargaining groups within the

company have increasingly balanced their pursuit of the traditional issue of finance and working conditions with an interest in furthering the survival and competitiveness of the company and the quality of the working lives of their employees."

This philosophy of involvement was then extended to the introduction of new technology and the intention was to use the loom building project as a pilot study as the following further quotation demonstrates:

"In seeking the involvement of shop floor personnel in the development of this technology, the Research and Technology Division proposed and obtained agreement to the adoption by a Company Council sub-committee of the role of overseer of the exercise - so that the potential benefits might be recognised and the concept, if proved effective, might be applied elsewhere."

From what began as a classical engineering approach to the development of manufacturing technology became a '*classical*' illustration of participation in job and system design. (See Figure 4.2, which summarises the phases in the development.)

The Research and Technology Division openly acknowledged that its initial approach had been one where engineers and work study specialists examined the needs and opportunities for change in loom building and the scope for mechanisation and automation of the tasks. The approach had been on a '*menu*' basis where the mystique and skill of the task of loom building had been systematically broken down into its constituent parts (eg '*cut wire*', '*strip wire*', '*lay wire on firm board*, etc) and to demonstrate how these could be mechanised.

However, the stage was reached where the various items of hardware could be drawn out on a single sheet of paper and arranged in a *cell* form, and to give the drawing scale they included human figures. This, as the quotation below from the Project Manager explains, prompted them to consider the working of the operators in detail.

"Despite having adopted the classical engineer's (people-less) approach to loom manufacture, we were sufficiently aware of the impact on the working lives of the loom builders to want to design their roles as part of the manufacturing system. We coined the term 'job design' before

Figure 4.2   Phases in development of loom technology

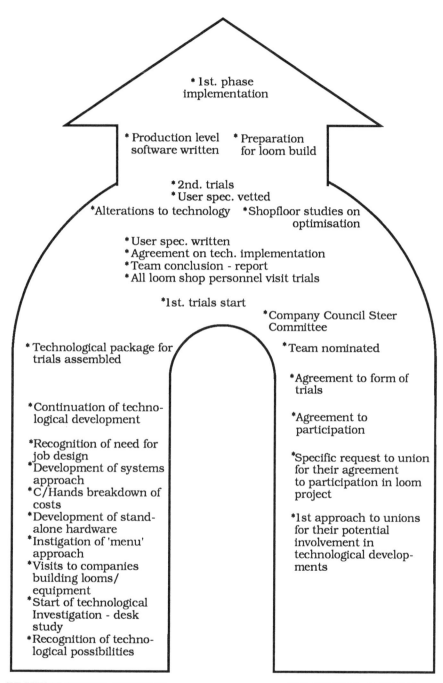

* 1st. phase
  implementation

* Production level   * Preparation
  software written   for loom build

* 2nd. trials
* User spec. vetted
*Alterations to technology   *Shopfloor studies on
                              optimisation

* User spec. written
* Agreement on tech. implementation
* Team conclusion - report
* All loom shop personnel visit trials

*1st. trials start

                              *Company Council Steer
                              Committee

* Technological package for   *Team nominated
  trials assembled

                              *Agreement to form of
                              trials

*Continuation of techno-   *Agreement to
  logical development   participation

*Recognition of need for
  job design   *Specific request to union
*Development of systems   for their agreement
  approach   to participation in loom
*C/Hands breakdown of   project
  costs
*Development of stand-   *1st approach to unions
  alone hardware   for their potential
*Instigation of 'menu'   involvement in
  approach   technological develop-
*Visits to companies   ments
  building looms/
  equipment
*Start of technological
  Investigation - desk
  study
*Recognition of techno-
  logical possibilities

TECHNOLOGICAL ASPECTS   **PERSONNEL ASPECTS**

39

realising that this was indeed the chosen title for the discipline of designing the job content and function of peoples' work lives."

4.5 A policy for future loom manufacture

The stage had now been reached where R & T, with the manufacturing division, could now propose the development of a policy for loom manufacture in the future. This policy consisted of two separate inter-related strands, one concerning the technology and the other concerning the people.

Regarding the technical development, as a result of its research, the company was now proposing an implementation of new technology in three phases:

Phase I - Manual loom building using computer-based instruction to the employees and automatic cable sorting.

In this process a continuous filament would be generated by a laser method and cut to length. A VDU would then take the operator through a step-by-step building sequence, eliminating the tedious sorting task, thereby offering a 30% improvement in productivity. The VDU screen would provide data showing the operator how to route the wires similar to the bunch sheet, which would give'*breakout*' data on the existing manual system.

Phase II - Manual loom building as outlined above, with the addition of automatic stripping and crimping of the majority of connectors.

In this process the machine would draw off the cable, recognising the end marks, cut the length, transport it to a terminating and inspection machine. The operator would then be supplied with a range of predetermined cables. This system, which was the preferred R & T option, would take the form of a manufacturing cell.

Phase III - Integrated systems, which would consist of automatic cable-laying machines, employing a robot and computer-controlled loom design and manufacture.

In this system the cables would be automatically cut to length, mechanically transferred via a laser stripper and automatic termination machine to a high-speed wire-laying machine. An automatic machine would prepare the forming boards from universal components and strap the bunches subsequent to laying.

These developments were seen as a long-term strategy and it was anticipated that full implementation would be over a six year time scale. However, the benefit in terms of increased productivity would be considerable and the time taken to build a loom would eventually be reduced from six weeks to four days.

In proposing these developments the Research and Technology Division recognised the essential contribution required from the shop floor where detailed knowledge and experience would be required to complement the technological possibilities.

Under the auspices of the Company Council and the sub-committee that had been formed as a Steering Group, agreement was obtained to release four shop floor operators with a chargehand, to be seconded to work with the R & T Division for a period of three months in the development of the new systems. The ultimate objective of this exercise would be the production of a User Specification as a basis for the future manufacturing process.

4.6 Job design in practice

The participants in this 'experiment' were nominated after consultation. The shop superintendent nominated a chargehand to participate and the shop steward nominated four operatives. In addition to this group, technologists from R & T were available to give support and adapt the hardware and software where required. Staff from design and quality were also identified to give specialist input and advice at regular intervals.

The development exercise which took place in the R & T building started with a three-day introductory programme in which presentations were given on all the projects and on the work completed during the investigation phase. Great emphasis was placed on the fact that the work was of an experimental nature and that the equipment and various systems were to be viewed as 'candidates ' and alternatives, rather than prescriptions for a future loom shop.

Following the introductory phase the group's task was to operate the various items of hardware in a 'stand-alone' mode to familiarise themselves with the equipment and provide feedback to R & T on their reactions and preferences. This was followed by a loom building phase in which members of the group took turns to perform the various tasks and observe. The building of the loom was accompanied by breaks in which suggestions were discussed, alterations made and feedback given to the design and quality staff and to line management.

4.7 Reaction of the loom builders

During the investigation at the company there was an opportunity to visit the existing loom shop and also to talk to those loom builders involved in the experiment and developments in R & T. At this stage, while the people in R & T were still exploring the options and alternatives, staff in the main loom shop had quite strong views on what was proposed.

Initial discussions were with the loom builders and other staff in the existing loom shop. Discussions were also held with the female operators who were cutting and crimping the wires manually in preparation for loom assembly. Their jobs which were very repetitive would be replaced by the new system which would carry out these operations automatically.

However, main discussions were with the skilled loom builders who assembled the looms, sorted out the wires and laid them out on the wiring looms. These discussions revealed both positive and negative reactions to the proposed changes. Their main concerns were that automation would result in deskilling and the creation of what they described as 'monkey jobs'. However, they recognised that the proposed system would help to create more orders and that they would get satisfaction from more involvement in the total business.

The current method of loom building was a one-person job and was particularly boring and there were frustrations with lack of parts and shortages. However, the individual was in charge of the building of the loom whereas each now felt that the computer would be controlling them. They felt very strongly that people need to control the computer and that they should determine the work order.

In describing their work with R & T the operators explained that while opportunities for mechanisation had been identified, there were some parts of the job that could not be automated. Also, it is the organisation of the work that takes the time rather than the work content. There were also many operations that had to be done to the wire before it would be released to the operator for laying.

However, apart from the issues and concerns expressed by the operators, it appeared that management also had concerns about the introduction of the new system. The manufacturing manager, apparently, was fearful of '*inanimate*' computer control of the whole system and managers feared the loss of their control to the computer programmers.

These reactions led those concerned with the experiment to conclude that it was the human factors rather than technical problems or hurdles that were determining the pace of change. It was explained to the author that, as a result of the user involvement described and the reactions and suggestions of the loom builders, the group had decided to opt for the less-ambitious system involving the supply of a continuous filament of wire, together with a VDU and printed instructions on how to lay the loom. With the bunching system the operator had to spend a lot of time sorting the job out, whereas now, with the new system, they could build up a loom at a walking pace, pressing the computer punch button to get their instructions.

The selling point of the new system was the speed of laying down the wire in a continuous filament. The next stage was to get the loom off the frame and to cut, bare and crimp the wires, and they were examining various automated machines to do these jobs. For this, they felt they needed the operators' involvement - not only in the detail, but also from a policy point of view and that this should be to consult with them rather than to tell them what was required.

Unfortunately, union attitudes towards external parties meant that it was not possible to obtain quantitative before-and-after measures regarding the changes to the job characteristics of the loom builders as a result of automation. However, from an informal discussion, it was possible to obtain some of their reactions and concerns on these issues.

Autonomy - as previously mentioned one of their main concerns was to retain their autonomy, ie not to be computer controlled. They therefore suggested that they should receive a computer tab or printout so that they themselves could decide which jobs to do and when.

Variety - similarly on the question of variety, they were very concerned about being stuck on one part of the operation. For example, they questioned why they couldn't install the completed harness in the aircraft and one is bound to ask why not!

Task identity - this would also be a reflection of the need to maintain task identity and involvement in the whole process.

Team work - some interest was also expressed in having more than one person working together on a loom. They felt that people were still basing the design on one person where there might be scope for more teamwork.

Feedback - finally, regarding feedback, they felt that the computer-based system did mean that they obtained quicker feedback on results and progress than before.

Clearly these suggestions and reactions had quite wide implications for both the organisation of the work and the technology. While a number were incorporated into the first phase of the development, eg the printout suggestion for retaining operator control, others could influence the shape of the further phases of development, eg Computer Aided Design and Manufacture (CAD/CAM) and operator involvement in installation.

5 NEW TECHNOLOGY AND ORGANISATION DEVELOPMENT

The loom building project was, in many senses, both an eye opener and a watershed, not only for the company, but also in terms of the author's own research. Whereas the FMS case demonstrates what can be achieved by alternative forms of work organisation alongside the new technology, the loom building case shows something about how to get there. Some of the questions from this project are as follows.

5.1 Questions arising from the loom building case

1. What role can 'choice' play in the introduction of computer systems? Can this concept be applied equally to the technology as to the organisational considerations involved?

2. What do we mean by job design in practice and who should be involved in the process? What does this case reveal about the value of a participative approach to job design?

3. What is the role of the technologist in introducing technological change? What factors and perspectives need to be taken into account if change is to be accepted and effective?

4. What does this case illustrate about organisational development in practice and what contribution can it make to the effective introduction of new technology?

5.2 Analysis of loom building project

The technology menu - one of the first points to emerge from this project is the concept of choice regarding both technology and organisation. Regarding technology, the R & T staff recognised that there were several options and alternatives that could be offered to the user. These were seen as *candidate* technology rather than prescriptions and that ultimately it was for the *users* to select what was appropriate and acceptable from the *menu* to satisfy their needs.

User involvement - fundamental to the *process* of the introduction of new technology in this case was the concept of *user* involvement. The user in this case included not only management, but also the trade unions and the shop floor. User involvement was seen to be necessary not only in terms of policy and at a strategic level via the senior management and the trade unions, but also at a detailed and operational level via line management and the operators themselves.

Job/system design as a development process - approached in this way the development of loom manufacture was as much a *process* of development as of design. While the company acknowledged that its initial approach was that of *classical engineering* and *technological determinism*, they equally acknowledged the ideas and suggestions of the shop floor and indeed felt that their contribution was essential to the development of an effective system.

Participants in the process - the loom building development group with its composition, connections and the umbrella of trade union support gave valuable clues as to those that need to be involved and have a stake and a contribution to make to the development process.

Shop floor influence/participation in job design - in analysing the loom building project, the Project Manager comments on "*the belief of the loom builders that they could improve the quality of their jobs*". They understood the potential of computers to eliminate the more boring elements of their work (they didn't like the *sorting task*).

In this they were proved right: they were able, to a large extent, to influence the form and function of the new work system by the input of their specialist knowledge and by tailoring the user specifications to suit their needs. "*To this extent*", the Project Manager suggests, "*the project was a successful job design exercise*".

The FMS case demonstrated that there are options and alternatives in both organisation and technical design. This loom building case demonstrates the options and alternatives that emerge during the process of technological change and some of the elements required in a strategy to achieve a satisfactory match between human and technological needs. Again, they learnt the hard way, but they actually learnt from the lessons and their experience influenced their future approach to technological change. They recognised that, as technologists, they needed to be aware of the human and social implications of the changes they were planning and to incorporate them into their developmental strategies.

> *"We began researching alternative loom building techniques and systems in the classical engineer's way - we sought to mechanise. But, fortunately for us, our realisation that a successful first phase required the participation of people who knew much more about how looms are made than we ever would, coincided with the discovery that they wished to be involved in the development of future work systems."*

This realisation stimulated a major change in the approach of R & T to its work and for the company to reconsider the potential of technology and job design for its future organisational development.

5.3 Role of technologist as a change agent
One of the most interesting features of this particular case study was the role played by the Project Manager and the changes in his outlook and personal development which occurred as a result of his involvement in the introduction of new technology.

Having come from an Engineering background and whilst not highly qualified (City & Guilds Certificate) he developed into a position of considerable responsibility as Project Manager in the Research and Technology Division. He was quick to recognise the significance of the work he was undertaking and sought opportunities to project and explore his ideas. He also registered the work for a CNAA M Phil and has more recently converted this to a PhD.

His involvement with R & T, and in particular with the loom shop project, appeared to influence him as an individual profoundly and he sought to extend this influence to others in the organisation from his role as Project Manager in R & T.

Following the loom project, he put forward proposals for a radically new approach to business improvement, cost reduction and technical change, involving both job design and organisational development. These proposals amounted to the development of an alternative strategy to the conventional approach to change which could be applied to a variety of potential problems, projects and developmental opportunities. These included for example the development of manufacturing Ilôts, employing group technology concepts to the use of job design at management level. Important and far reaching though these potential projects might have been, of more significance was the suggested approach that should be adopted to their implementation.

5.4 Changing business strategy

A number of factors came together which highlight the relevance of job design and organisation development to business improvement and the use of new technology. The company had traditionally operated in a cost-plus environment where there was a lack of aggressive commercialisation and of targets for both design and cost. However, increasing international competition, the opening up of the civil aircraft market and the introduction of fixed price contracts were forcing the company to become more competitive and cost effective.

The company responded to the changing business environment by off-loading its sales operation and creating a marketing division and market-orientated business group. Cost targets and reporting structures were introduced in order to control operating costs and emphasis was placed on the potential of new technology for improving cost efficiency. They also recognised its threat to their autonomy and vigorously sought to preserve this in the way the new system was designed. Like others such as Howard Rosenbrock (1981), the case does provide evidence of how computers can be used to provide staff with information to enable them to control the process more effectively rather than be controlled by it.

5.5 Technology as a catalyst for change

The case also provides valuable evidence of the potential of technology as a catalyst for change. The Project Manager describes how the operators were initially sceptical that machines could ever do their jobs. However, he felt their immersion at R & T made them recognise the inevitability of technical change and of the temporariness of their current job situation. This, he suggested, helped in their acceptance and co-operation in the change process.

Thus, as the Project Manager proposed, we need to recognise the capacity or *latent heat* of technology to facilitate change through a process of unfreezing existing attitudes, changing and refreezing.

On this latter point it may well be that while some consolidation is necessary to accept and work with a new situation, it is dangerous if attitudes do become refrozen. Perhaps what is required are people and forms of work organisation which are capable of continuous adaptation to change and organisational renewal. This clearly calls for very different skills and attitudes amongst those involved in the process and a distinct departure from the traditional emphasis on narrow technical skills.

5.6 Role of organisational development in technological change

Analysis of both these cases does highlight the relevance of organisational development to the introduction of new technology.

We need to recognise the organisation as an open socio-technical system subject to pressures and changes in the external environment. It is comprised of overlapping, interlocking sub-systems, which helps to explain the issues involved in the introduction of technological change. Each specialist is, to some extent, working as a change agent between the organisation and its environment (see Figure 5.1)

Thus, as can be seen, the personnel specialist endeavours to adapt the organisational, personnel and employment policies and practices to changing requirements and demands. Technologists attempt to adapt an organisation's manufacturing and information systems to the latest technology.

The conventional 1960's view of OD was that the OD consultant would intervene largely on the organisational variables and then changes would follow in the other three. However, as Clark (1972) and others point out, OD has been criticised for assuming that it is possible to introduce change successfully by intervening on one variable alone. For successful change he argues that analysis of the requirements for change should be conducted on all the relevant variables. Thus, while change may be initiated by changing technology it is necessary to analyse and take into account the corresponding changes that may be required in terms of the task, the people and the organisation.

This suggests that change, rather than being seen as a specific isolated event, needs to be seen as a process of analysis and adaptation, where communication and interaction and an understanding of each other's perspectives is essential. This certainly supports and reinforces the need for wider rather than narrow representation in the process of introducing technical changes and for an interactive and participative approach to the process.

Figure 5.1 The enterprise and its environment

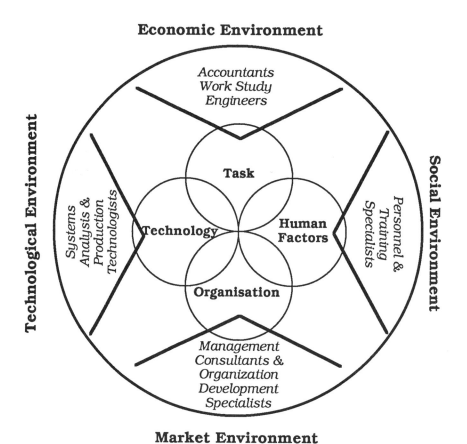

50

6   ORGANISATION, MANAGEMENT AND TECHNOLOGICAL CHANGE

6.1 Organisation and management implications

Whilst the starting point for this research was at the level of the individual, the impact of new technology on peoples' jobs and the potential contribution job design can make to its effective introduction, the results of our investigations confirm that the issues concerned are much wider than this. The results of the author's earlier work (Bailey, 1983) contained much about the wider impact of job and work organisation changes on such aspects as the structure and style of the organisation, reward and control systems and the role of management and supervision.

In looking at some of the wider issues, writers such as Schumacher (1973) and Galbraith (1971) draw our attention to the concept that '*small is beautiful*' and that if we can organise big business in this way it can help to overcome some of the human problems that create a 'drag' on organisational effectiveness and human growth. Whereas, until recent times, mainframe computers had reinforced the trend towards centralisation, the availability of microcomputers encourages decentralisation of control and decision making through the formation of smaller more autonomous units.

This, together with the recognition that such forms of organisation may be more appropriate in the changing environment of business, is seen as an important ingredient of a company's 'strategic choice' (Child 1972).   In this respect Trist (1981) draws attention to the opportunities that are created by new technology and green field sites for more fundamental and stepped changes in attitudes and organisation.

However, whether these opportunities are taken is very much in the hands of management. Williamson (1983) provides evidence of managements' fear of loss of control as a result of the introduction of new technology. Buchanan and Boddy (1983) in their studies of organisations and the computer age show the influences of management attitudes on the way in which new technology is introduced and the forms of work organisation adopted. This lends support to the view that the negative human consequences of new technology, particularly in terms of reducing job satisfaction, are not so much as a result of the technology itself, but of management attitudes towards technology and towards people and their involvement.

The latter's studies of technological change in biscuit making and an engineering consultancy firm (see Chapter 2. section 2.8) explain the effect that different approaches to work organisation has on either distancing people from the technology or enabling the technology to complement the people. In this sense, management have choices in how to approach the introduction of the technology.

In an article entitled "What's new in job design' Wall (1984) suggests that changes in technology not only imply changes in job content and job design, but also in terms of organisation and management. There were big implications for the job of the supervisor, the need for supervision and for changes in the role of management. The emphasis, it is suggested, is towards more self-management and decision making by the individual and/or work group and a tendency towards a flatter, more decentralised structure.

This greater autonomy raises its own problems and demands. It is not a question of abdication by management, but of delegation. People need a replacement for the direction and control they were used to receiving in the form of clearer objectives and feedback so that they can manage themselves. There can be problems of discipline and control when some individuals take advantage of the more organic situation, and when colleagues do not want to 'shop their mates'. There is therefore a need for clearer guidance and a framework of operation in terms of standards for such things as quality, housekeeping, safety, etc. New technology may call for new forms of organisation and management, and this can add up to the need for a change in the whole style and philosophy of the organisation from the traditional situation of specialisation, centralisation, direction and control.

Organisations exemplifying some of these characteristics were described by Trist (1981) in a paper on the evolution of socio-technical systems. This paper demonstrates the relevance of socio-technical systems thinking and design concepts to the introduction of new technology. Having described the birth of socio-technical systems design processes (Hill 1971), Trist illustrates its then recent application in the development of new plant mostly in the USA. Where social aspects of the plants operation were considered much earlier, the joint optimisation of socio-technical design can be better achieved.

These plants with well developed primary work systems have fewer levels, functions and management personnel than conventional plants. The numbers in the workforce were also lower and payment was based on knowledge rather than on the work that people were currently doing. Foremen were non-existent or became facilitators, trainers or forward planners. Information was shared for problem solving purposes rather than for management control purposes. These plants were learning systems and involved the principle of minimum initial specification to allow the progressive involvement of those concerned at all levels.

This led to a new organisational paradigm (see Figure 6.1) which, with its flexibility and efficiency in terms of resource utilisation, is considered to be appropriate to the resulting turbulent environment.

Figure 6.1   Organisational paradigms (Trist 1981)

Old Paradigm	New Paradigm
The technological imperative	Joint optimisation
Man as an extension of the machine	Man as complementary to the machine
Man as an expendable spare part	Man as a resource to be developed
Maximum task breakdown, simple narrow skills	Optimum task grouping, multiple broad skills
External controls (supervisors, specialist staffs, procedures)	Internal controls (self-regulating subsystems)
Tall organisation chart, autocratic style	Flat organisation chart, participative style
Competition, gamesmanship	Collaboration, collegiality
Organisation's purposes only	Members' and society's purposes only
Alienation	Commitment
Low risk-taking	Innovation

6.2 Management of change

These ideas are reinforced in a more recent article by Hans Van Beinum (1988) entitled "New Technology and Organisational Choice". He suggests that the scope and scale of technological change is such as to call for a new paradigm of organisation. In designing adaptive systems he argues that there are basically only two choices in the way that an organisation designs redundancy into its system. Unless an organisation does have redundancy or over-capacity it cannot have the flexibility to adapt to the changes in the environment required.

The two choices of redundancy of parts, or redundancy of functions, are, he suggests, based on two quite different value systems. The first option is for people to have narrowly based individual tasks like replaceable parts of the machine. The basic building block is the individual and parts have to be added to the system for the purposes of control and backed up or replaced when they fail. This results in the characteristically mechanistic, bureaucratic and hierarchical systems of much of industry today. This contrasts, however, with the second option which is based on redundancy of functions, recognising the multiple capacities of people and their ability to cope with complex roles. Here, rather than adding additional parts, additional functions are added to the individual. This develops the individual's ability to handle a wide range of roles and their capacity for self control. The building block in this instance is not the individual, but the self-managing group.

These alternative values represent a different concept of organisation as is illustrated in Figure 6.2 and amounts to what the author describes as a new paradigm of organisation. However, it is recognised that while such new concepts of organisation may well be required, they are far from easy to introduce. The transformation from the old to the new requires nothing less than the working out of a new organisational philosophy!

This, Trist argues, is more than simply methods and techniques but involves questions of basic values and assumptions. Whereas the old philosophy was based on technology and bureaucracy, the new philosophy is based on socio-ecological and participative principles. He emphasises the need for change to be initiated at the strategic level in the organisation and sees a value in drawing together the work analysis and organisational development traditions.

Figure 6.2   New organisational paradigm

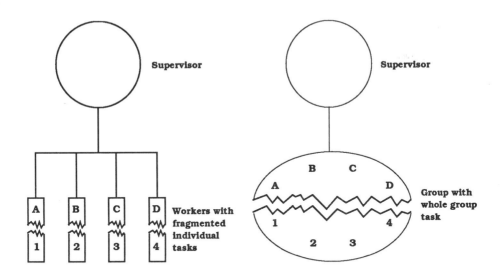

Characteristics of the old paradigm	Characteristics of the new paradigm
* redundancy of parts	* redundancy of functions
* emphasis on external coordination and control	* emphasis on internal coordination and control
* fragmented socio-technical system	* joint optimisation of socio-technical system
* technological imperative - man as extension of machine, a commodity	* man is complementary to machine and a resource to be developed
* organisation design based on total specificatiion	* organisation design based on minimum critical specificatiion
* maximum task breakdown, narrow skills	* optimum task grouping, multiple broad skills
* building block is one person - one task	* building block is self-managing group
* alienation	* involvement and commitment

In this context Birchall and Carnall (1974) discuss the need for a strategy in planning and designing technological change and Cherns (1973) discusses the role of action research in facilitating the process. However, in terms of change, Davis (1979) draws attention to the role of the systems analyst and production engineer as a change agent and the importance of involving behavioural perspectives at the earliest stage of this change process.   Mumford (1976) draws attention to the value of user involvement in the design process in what she describes as a participative approach to systems design.   Clark (1972), when discussing the role of organisational development in making change, draws attention to the need for interaction on all the key organisational variables, namely economic, technical and social.   Organisational development, he argues, has been criticised in the past for seeking to achieve change by intervening on the social factors above.

Thus, we can see that management of technological change is not just about changes in the technology or the social system, but in all of the relevant and inter-related variables. It is not just about changes in operational efficiency, but also in the organisation's strategic response to its environment. Finally, it is not about the arbitrary imposition of new systems, but through involvement and participation is a process of developing a new solution involving changes to technology, people and structure, to meet the changing task. This, as Trist suggests, is nothing short of developing a new philosophy of management and organisation and a radical change in the organisation's culture.

6.3 Strategy and technology

Whilst much of the impetus for change in terms of job design and technology arises from internal requirements for increased motivation and efficiency and is related to issues of effective operations management, the link between these developments and the strategy of the firm becomes increasingly evident.

In today's complex and turbulent environment the criteria for survival and organisational effectiveness are changing. While it is clearly important for an organisation to make a profit in order to survive, this is only as a consequence of doing the other things that are expected of it. Consequently the stakeholder concept of organisational effectiveness emphasises that survival of an organisation depends on its continuing ability to satisfy the expectations of all its stakeholders, not just the shareholders (Johnson and Scholes 1984). Thus the customer's concern for quality, choice and service, the employee's concern for involvement and personal development, and the community's concern for social and environmental responsibility, need to be reflected in the organisation's strategy and plans.

Ideas on these issues are reinforced by current thinking and research in the field of the strategic management of change (Pettigrew 1987). In reviewing the changes affecting the field of business policy and strategic management, Pettigrew draws attention to the need for management to have the confidence and capability to sense, articulate and implement major changes in business strategy, structure, culture and people, in order to ensure business success. There is, he suggests, some scepticism towards the more formal strategic planning methods and an increased sensitivity towards the more informal processes of leadership, vision building, communications, team and commitment building as means of managing strategic change. Strategic change, he argues, involves change in the culture and the structure, as well as product market and geographical positioning.

The question about strategy is whether it is seen as an endogenous or exogenous process, whether one should start with the firm or the environment it is operating in. Current thinking would seem to suggest that one is dealing not only with questions relating to 'content and choice' and the analytical processes involved, but also with 'process' and the management of change and the context in which it occurs. Thus strategic change is about both the 'why' and the 'how'.

These ideas are usefully summarised by Pettigrew in an analytical model (see Figure 6.3) relating content and process to context in the field of strategic change. In this figure the outer context refers to the economic, business, social and political formations in which the firm operates, while the inner refers to structure, culture and political context. While content refers to the decision and choices about strategy, process refers to the actions, reactions and interactions of the interested parties as they move the firm from its present to its future state.

Figure 6.3 Analytical model of strategic change (after Pettigrew)

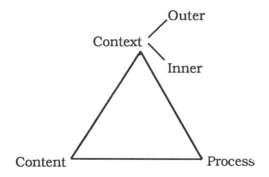

In these circumstances, strategy and its development needs to be seen more as an integral part of the job of management, and the organisation itself needs to be strategic in order to respond.

The introduction of new technology in the form of automated manufacturing systems and of computer based information systems can greatly enhance this process, but only if management appreciate the opportunities and links between the two. The development of these systems can release management from many of the day-to-day operating problems to concentrate more on the strategic management of change which is arguably what their job should really be about. Often technology is introduced for purely operational reasons, to minimise costs and the human contribution. In today's circumstances, we need the effective involvement of both people and technology to provide the service and quality the customer requires.

However, changes in social structure, and in the values reflected in it, may be more difficult to accomplish than those of technology. As long ago as 1965, Emery and Trist (1965) suggested that with the way that the environment was developing, with changes not only in terms of computerisation, but of the 'ground' itself, the only way of exerting control was through the development of commonly held values. However, the development of new values was a social process which could take as much as a generation to develop which, they suggested, proved a challenge to the social scientist if the rapid change needed was to be accomplished.

These issues are quite graphically illustrated in the following two case studies which form the next stage of our investigation.

PART III

IMPACT OF AUTOMATION
AND COMPUTERISATION

7 AUTOMATION AND JOB SATISFACTION - A CASE STUDY OF AN AUTOMATED PAINT SPRAYING PLANT

7.1 Background to the case study

The opportunity to study this case arose from the author's involvement in and initiation of a Teaching Company Scheme aimed at assisting smaller companies to utilise the benefits of micro-technology. Of the four companies that participated two were involved in applying micro-processors to their products, one to their management and cost control system and the fourth on which this case is based to their manufacturing process.

Following a feasibility study of the automation of their paint spraying facility involving the use of a robot and encouraged by the availability of a DTI grant, the company concerned decided to proceed and a Teaching Company Associate was appointed to join the scheme and work on this and other projects with the firm. The author's involvement as a co-ordinator of the scheme provided an opportunity to study and hopefully influence the introduction of the new system as it appeared that it could be a very valuable example of the introduction of new technology in manufacturing.

Data for the paint spraying case was collected over a period of 18 months from a variety of sources. Involvement in the teaching company scheme meant that it was possible to obtain access to company information and reports on the proposed scheme. In addition, as tutor to the associate involved, the author was able to obtain information and impressions from his involvement with the project and to attend one of the planning meetings for the system.

Interviews were held with the Managing Director, Production Director, and

Production Manager about their objectives and plans in introducing the new system. In addition, the consultant concerned with the robot was interviewed and also the project co-ordinator to obtain their impressions of the project. Finally, interviews were held with the existing paint shop supervisor and the operators to obtain their opinions about the new system and the advantages and benefits they felt it would afford.

With the consent of the company a survey was carried out of the existing paint shop operators, using the Hackman and Oldham Survey. The results of this survey were fed back to management. Once the new system was in operation regular visits to the firm were made to establish how it was working out. Apart from interviews with the Production Director, Production Manager, and Paint Shop Supervisors, a follow-up survey was carried out with the remaining paint sprayers. Again, the Hackman and Oldham survey was utilised, together with group discussions to discuss the results and its implications.

Although there were changes of both Production Director and Paint Shop Supervisor during the period, it proved possible to obtain an invaluable insight into the process of change involved on a before-and-after basis.

The author's role, therefore, in practice, became one of observation and as the firm were involved with the local Polytechnic as a Teaching Company no real constraints were placed on the information that could be obtained. As a result of this, it was possible to follow the introduction through from early stages in the planning process, through implementation and subsequent operation and evaluation. During the period of involvement with the company the opportunity was taken to make a video to be used for teaching purposes. This followed the introduction of the new system from its inception, through to its introduction and eventual operation. The data from this video, and the transcripts of the interviews involved, also provided invaluable information and impressions for the research. In addition, a paper based on this project was presented and published at an international conference on Organisation and New Technology in Budapest (ref. Bailey 86). This paper forms the basis of the rest of the chapter.

7.2 Background to the company and introduction of the new system

The company employs approximately 130 people in a small market town and although relatively autonomous was at the time part of a larger group. It manufactures a range of mechanical equipment and recently had a vigorous programme of new product development; it had also been investing in new production technology including a computer-controlled punch press machine and CNC press brakes.

Paint spraying

Paint spraying in this, as in many companies, appears to be a dirty and unhealthy job. The operators work in individual booths with considerable over-spray which, without masks, presents a health hazard. Although the feeling in the shop was of *camaraderie* the physical conditions left something to be desired and these conditions were an important reason for the change.

The robot project

With the current level of expansion of about 25% per annum, the company recognised that the capacity of the existing paint shop would become inadequate to maintain a supply of sprayed components and some change would be necessary. Following the feasibility study, the company decided to opt for an automated system employing a robot and powder paint technology which, it was felt, would not only cope with the additional capacity required, but through savings on direct labour, would improve profitability on the higher level of throughput. The potential benefits of the new system were seen to be:

1. Improved and consistent quality
2. Improved toughness and cosmetic appearance
3. Increased production capacity
4. Better labour utilisation
5. Removal of unhealthy and unsocial task of manual spraying
6. The company would qualify for a government grant.

The development of the new system was undertaken by a firm of consultants who were experienced in robotics and were contracted to supervise the project from initial concept to the commissioning of the new plant. In conjunction with nominated suppliers for the robot, conveyors and spray booths, the new system was planned and targeted installation was to be during the normal shut-down in the summer.

The new system involved departure from individual manual wet spray booths to an automated system employing powder spraying technology.

63

The new system was based on a conveyor which after degreasing passed components through two automated spray booths with oscillating spray nozzles. The robot automatically touched up corners that the oscillators could not reach and the components were then passed through the oven for final unloading and inspection. The speed of the line was fixed and the robot was controlled by programmes inserted in the computer control console. A certain amount of manual touching up was still required.

Considerable effort was put in by the company to plan the introduction of the new system in advance. Apart from the feasibility study staff were informed as much as two years in advance of the intentions. This enabled the company to avoid any redundancies. A moratorium on external recruitment had been in operation for twelve months prior to the change.

While the then Production Director had some experience of these systems the company took the precaution of employing another firm of external consultants to act as a safeguard and to try to ensure that all aspects were anticipated and planned for. In the event the new system was installed as planned and production commenced immediately after the shut-down.

In economic terms, the project appeared to have been very successful. Quality, though of a slightly lower standard, had proved consistent, and the appearance and durability of the product were satisfactory, according to the production manager. The increased capacity had been created and substantial savings on direct labour had been obtained. Operating costs of materials, energy and jigs increased, but these were, according to the company, more than outweighed by the labour savings.

A number of technical problems were experienced initially, especially with the robot with problems of static, synchronisation with the track and with programming, although these were overcome as people gained experience and were able to make more effective use of the robot.

Physical conditions still presented some problems in terms particularly of excessive heat and drifting powder spray. However, the changes in the nature of the work and of sources of job satisfaction require closer examination.

7.3 Changes in work organisation

Manual system

The original manual system was based on the concept of one-man one-job and there was a coincidence between the *task* and *job* boundaries (see Figure 7.1 for socio-technical analysis of the original manual system). Here, apart from the degreaser which was established as an independent job, the paint sprayers worked as individuals in an individual spray booth and, operating with a fairly high degree of discretion, performed a complete task with the exception of inspection which came under a different department. There was little if any need for interaction other than on a social plane and the role of the supervisor was concerned with work allocation scheduling and progress chasing.

Automated system

On the new automated system (see Figure 7.2) the inspection function had been incorporated into the department and it was generally felt that the automated system made consistency in quality standards easier to maintain. Maintenance was functionally separate, as in the manual system, although there was increasing evidence of involvement in production planning and maintenance issues (possibly against the policy of the production manager).

Task allocation

Despite the original policy of encouraging job rotation the operators were allowed by the previous supervisor to gravitate to particular jobs (possibly due at least in part to the fact that they had always had individual jobs before and felt more secure in this situation). Each job on the new system necessarily represented only a small part of the total task of spraying a component, eg degreasing, loading, touching up, unloading and inspection.

Changes in job content and satisfaction

With the agreement of the Management Director, a survey was carried out to assess the attitudes of the paint sprayers to their jobs at the time and how they felt they might be affected by the new system. From this survey it appeared that, while the operators would welcome the new system for the improvements in hygiene and working conditions that it would afford, concern was expressed at the potential loss in job satisfaction as a result of the robot and automation.

Figure 7.1 Old system

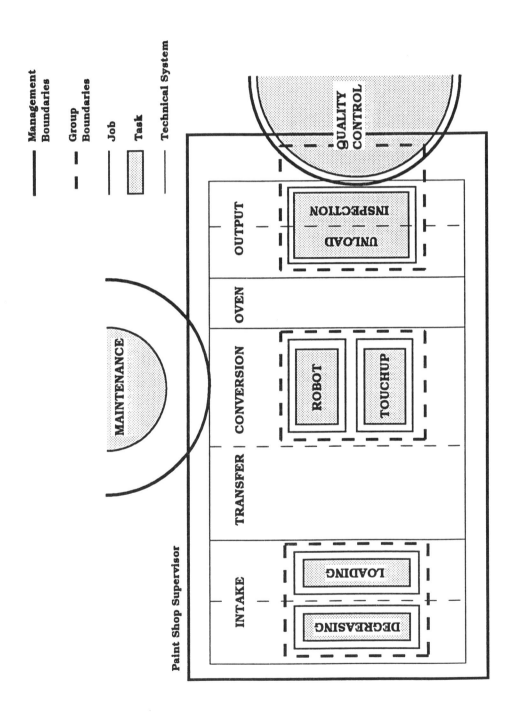

Figure 7.2   New system

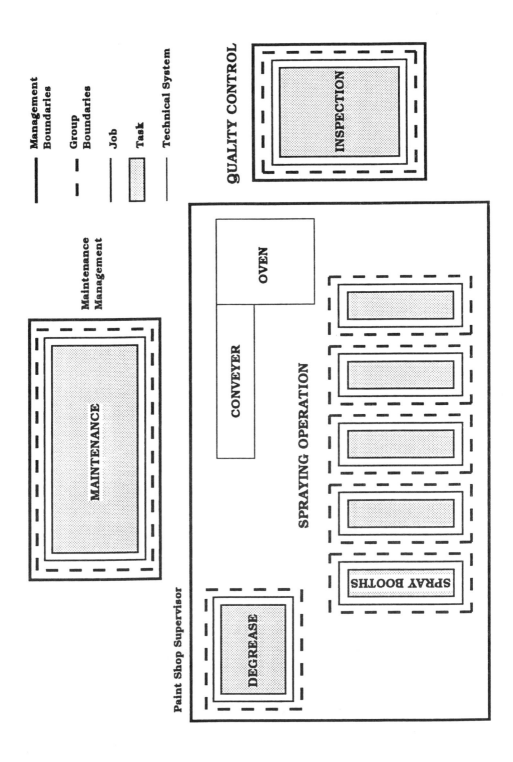

The survey showed that, despite the existing working conditions, people experienced a considerable degree of job satisfaction from their feeling that the job was important and that they could exercise some degree of discretion as to how they did the job. Also they obtained direct feedback on the quality of their own work.

In the new situation they feared a loss of variety and demand for their skills. The job would be predetermined and they would not feel involved in the total task. Also in the new system they feared that they would not obtain the direct feedback on quality.

Their preference, which coincided with management's own views, was that a system of job rotation would help to overcome some of these deficiencies and help to restore some of the variety and the sense of involvement in the total task that they had been accustomed to.

Installation of the new system
The new system was installed during the shut-down and, apart from initial problems in getting the robot working, production commenced. At this stage, despite some disillusionment with the robot, the operators co-operated with whatever was necessary to keep production going and a lot of hand spraying was required to compensate for the robot.

The consultants were absent from the scene for a quite long period and some difficulty was experienced in securing their assistance in getting the new system operating effectively. However, the supervisor and the leading hand got involved in sorting out the programming problems themselves.

In the meantime, the staffing on the line had been reduced to four plus a leading hand and supervisor as opposed to the 14 people previously employed (on a two-shift basis). At this stage no group approach to work organisation had emerged and job rotation had not been initiated, one person being 'stuck on unloading for 10 days at a stretch'. It was also proposed by the production manager that one person should be employed on inspection in order to monitor the standard required rather than everybody being involved in achieving the quality standard.

7.4 Effects on job content and job satisfaction
Whilst largely successful in economic and technical terms, there was a complete change in the nature of the task from a skilled paint spraying job

to one of largely machine minding. This led to a marked deterioration in the quality of work experienced by people in the new system for both the operators and supervisor alike and resulted in a decline in morale.

Job rotation was limited mainly to touching up and the operators were confined to what some of them felt were 'mindlessly boring' jobs. Several people commented that they could not believe how slowly time was passing, and that when they thought it was lunch time it was still only 10.00 o'clock in the morning. They found the standing around very tiring on the legs and would all have preferred to be spraying manually despite the physical conditions. The operators themselves felt that the new system was no quicker and that the robot was not touching up properly.

These views were to a large extent echoed by the supervisor at the time who felt that the interest had gone out of the job. He resented the fact that he was denied involvement with maintenance and programming aspects of the new system which would have been for him a source of new interest and skills.

Although there were some individual variations in response, eg from the person doing the tacking compared to the loading job, it was generally felt that the boredom was undesirable and that people's attention inevitably wandered with consequent dangers for safety and for the quality of work.

With the aid of the Hackman and Oldham questionnaire and subsequent discussions a detailed analysis was made of the changes which showed some deterioration on all motivational characteristics of the paint sprayer's jobs (see Figure 7.3).

In terms of *variety* there was no choice of the components to be sprayed as this was determined by the computer. *Task identity* decreased because they felt nobody was involved in the total task. *Discretion* also declined because whereas before people would determine their own pace of work this was now dictated by the speed of the track over which the operators had no control. Similarly, on the question of *feedback*, whereas operators could previously derive feedback on the quality of their work they now felt it didn't matter.

Although the person working on degreasing felt he had some contact with other people, the other operators felt relatively isolated in their position on

Figure 7.3 Changes to job characteristics/profile of paint sprayers as a result of automation

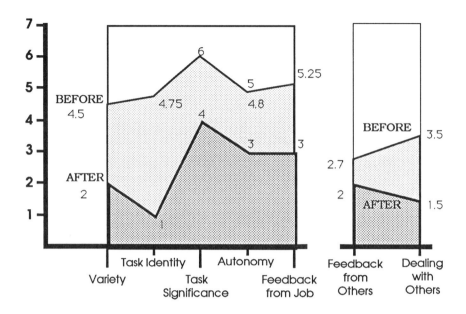

the line and satisfaction with the social aspects of the job had failed quite significantly.

Although people went into the change with an open mind, initial reactions to the new system were not very favourable. Some people expressed the view that it would be better if the line were totally automated as their jobs at present could be performed by 'monkeys'. It would certainly appear that in most cases the people employed on the new line were over qualified for the work that they were now doing which was essentially machine minding and would seek the earliest opportunity for transfer or alternative employment unless some changes were made.

7.5 Operator involvement and teamwork

Whilst on the basis of individual jobs involvement had clearly declined, there was some indication that this could be restored to a degree by the development of group or teamwork. At the point of changeover, for example from one component or paint colour to another, operators could have some influence over the system, eg when an operator managed to get the changeover down to 20 minutes, he said to the supervisor 'we showed em Big D'. Clearly at this level there are many issues over which the group could have influence. They had discretion to influence quality within the given limits of the quality standard and there is also evidence that they had some influence in the area of maintenance which could arguably become their responsibility to some extent.

Another important aspect was the involvement of the operators in lead teaching the robot in the production of new spraying programmes. In this way their skills were used and, to some extent, maintained and incorporated into the new system. Some 22 programmes were developed and sometimes as many as six attempts were required before a programme was perfected.

Arising from this there is the question of the retention of paint spraying skill on the section. Since the quality of the programmes produced reflected the skill of the paint sprayers it was important that these skills were maintained. To some extent this could be achieved by maintaining a manual facility primarily for touching up, but without the skilled paint sprayers it would be difficult to develop satisfactory programmes.

7.6 Role of the supervision and management style
The previous supervisor decided to leave partly because of the dispute over his involvement in the programming and maintenance aspects of the new equipment. In the view of the newly appointed supervisor the new system called for teamwork. He stressed the fact that if one person does not do his job properly, eg loading, this affects others and the performance of the line. He argued that interaction was required between the operators on a problem solving basis and saw it as his role to develop this. There was increasing evidence of a positive desire on the part of the operators to become involved in the performance of the whole system, and the supervisor intended to initiate fortnightly meetings to discuss progress and problems with the group. There is therefore some evidence of an 'incipient' group forming as a matter of necessity to cope with the nature of the new technical system, which in many ways resembles a process plant in which group working is accepted practice.

The role of the supervisor had changed considerably as a result of the change in the technology. Previously his job was very much involved with scheduling and allocating work and with problem solving and co-ordination within the section. It also involved co-ordination between the jobs in the system as well as between his section and others in the factory, namely maintenance, quality and production planning. This left relatively little time for his man management role and communications suffered as a result.

With the new system the programming was done by the Production Manager and scheduling of the work was largely predetermined. The supervisor, therefore, had more time for communications and man management as well as for exercising his boundary management role. Here again the fact that responsibility for quality control was now incorporated into the department made him more autonomous and independent. He was now becoming more of a representative to management of the group's ideas and suggestions for improvements, eg showers to overcome paint drift problems and improvements to the design of jigs. Even without the development of job rotation, the institution of regular group meetings and the creation of a teamwork climate did much to enhance the operator's sense of involvement in the whole process. In fact, the supervisor was in favour of job rotation for example to help people identify more readily with the quality standard required although they were aware of what this was. Thus, the supervisor was increasingly taking on the role of social development in the new system.

Whereas there appears to have been a decisive move with the appointment of the new supervisor to a more employee-centred approach in terms of management style, there is evidence of increased differentiation regarding the different aspects of management tasks in the paint shop.

Whereas previously the supervisor largely controlled the programming and scheduling of the work in the shop, this control passed to the Production Manager who did not appear to have a great deal of direct contact with the paint shop or its problems. The supervisor retained and had developed his role in people management.

The Leading Hand, who was previously involved with inspection and direct supervision of the paint sprayers, had now become the main specialist in the programming of the robot, control of the console and some aspects of maintenance of the equipment. This provided him with increased job interest and had, in effect, given him control over the technical aspects of management in the paint shop.

There is also some evidence of conflicts across the boundary between the paint shop and the rest of the factory in that the demands for changes in components and paint colours conflicted with the needs of the new system for relatively long runs. Constant changes were seen as disruptive by the paint shop supervisor but may on the other hand be vital in meeting changing customer needs. There was therefore some conflict between the requirements of the system for flexibility and for productivity. As already indicated this is a particular area in which the people on the systems can make a contribution to both aims by achieving more rapid changeover times, therefore minimising the losses to production.

7.7 Discussion

This case does demonstrate quite clearly the impact that new technology can have on the content of people's jobs. Here a responsible employer had taken considerable steps to ensure that no redundancies would occur as a result of automation. *'I personally am a great believer that automation doesn't reduce your labour force if you can plan it in the right manner.'* (Managing Director)

Equally, they took their responsibilities for communication and consultation seriously: *'there weren't any secrets about what we were trying to do - that we were trying to reduce our commitment to manpower in that shop'.*

However, regarding work organisation there is evidence of a lack of planning. Understandably, the company's initial concerns while planning the new system were the solution of technical problems and ensuring that the system was installed on time in order that production could be maintained. Thus the discussion in the planning group, which was composed largely of component suppliers and technical consultants plus company management and supervision, concentrated on those issues. The planning meetings were dominated by the technical consultants and as one said *'All the subjects that have been discussed have been basically technical and any management problems they've got are internal'*.

It was felt that management problems would only arise if the unions were brought into the discussions, and it was generally felt that these were well within the competence of the firm to resolve internally. Some discussion took place on training, not for the operators, but for the supervisor and it was arranged for the supervisor and leading hand to attend a course on the robot. (In the event they attended the maintenance rather than the operating course due to an administrative error.) In view of this, the existing personnel have had to learn how to operate the equipment themselves and even now do not possess any manual or operating instructions.

At the planning stage, the issue of what form the structure of jobs on the new system should take was left open. The Production Director at the time felt it better to allow this to sort itself out once the system was running and that all hands might well be needed during the first stages of its operation.

Understandably primary concern was on the operation of the new system from a technical and production point of view. Whilst it was felt that some form of job rotation would be desirable the policy was adopted not to make any decisions on this until the new system was in operation .

In the event, quite significant features and unanticipated consequences occurred on the social side of the new system. Although it is questionable how many of them could have been anticipated, it is clear that a price was paid for the omission of the consideration of human factors at the early stages of planning.

In practice, once the new system was in operation, people gravitated to the jobs they knew or liked and as time went on, with the preoccupation of the supervisor with the technical problems of programming and working on the line himself to keep production up, any such issues appeared to be overlooked, making any changes to work organisation now more difficult to introduce.

With a computer automated system and group technology, group forms of organisation may be required if a satisfactory match between human and technological factors is to be obtained. However, this conflicts with the accepted concepts of work organisation in the firm where up until now the norm of one-man one-job and control by management and supervision have predominated.

The extent to which these problems can be overcome may to some extent be influenced by the approach adopted to the introduction of technological change, ie the 'who, what, when and why' questions. For instance, the discussions on the paint spraying system were dominated by engineers who perhaps by training and to some extent by disposition are orientated towards technical and economic factors rather than human factors. This has implications for their training and/or the role of social sciences in the planning process.

As regards the issues discussed during the planning phase, ie the 'what' factors, it would appear that insufficient weight was given to the human factors, particularly relating to work organisation, for a satisfactory match between human and technological needs to be achieved. The policy of allowing it to sort itself out after the event does not seem to have worked very well.

To have achieved a satisfactory match it would seem important that these issues be given equal weight and considered at the earliest possible stage in the planning process. This would also have had the merit of allowing some adaptation of the technical system to fit the people. (For example, the opportunity for the operators to be involved in correcting the tapes was inhibited by the layout of the plant.) The question of why this did not happen will be taken up in the next chapter.

8   ANALYSIS OF THE PAINT SPRAYING CASE

This case study does provide some invaluable evidence regarding some of the key issues in the introduction of new technology and technological change. In particular, it highlights some of the factors which may represent constraints in achieving a satisfactory match between the task and technology variables and those concerned with organisation and people. Some of these issues are posed in the following questions and subsequent analysis of this case.

8.1 Questions and issues raised by the case

1. What light does this case throw on the potential conflict between operational efficiency and the need for flexibility? What are the links between business strategy and the role of new technology?

2. What influence did the composition of the planning team have on the design process and ultimate solution? Who should be involved at the planning stage?

3. What does the case reveal about the effects of automation on job satisfaction? What contribution could job design and alternative forms of work organisation have made in this situation?

4. What evidence does this case provide regarding the changes to the role of supervision in automated systems?

5. What influence did the prevailing management attitudes have over the design solution chosen in this case? How far could alternative models and solutions have been adopted in this situation?

8.2 New technology and business strategy

One of the key issues brought out in this case is the potential conflict between the operational requirements for increased efficiency against the strategic need for greater flexibility.

The stated reasons and objectives for introducing the automated paint spraying plant were to do with increased capacity and productivity. With the expansion of the business, the company recognised the need for increased painting capacity. They recognised the opportunity that new technology provided to achieve this goal, while holding costs down through savings in direct labour.

However, the company was operating in quite a diverse market and had for some time had a relatively vigorous programme of new product development. Although a substantial part of their business involved producing machines for one major customer there was a variety of other products and machines involving components that needed painting.

In the event the system proved to be very inflexible and the need for manual, off-line spraying had to be increased in order to cope with this demand. In fact the consultants in charge of the programme criticised the company for introducing new products and thus changing the specification of the system. This was despite a comment from the Production Director that "what we have here is a Flexible Manufacturing System!"

This demonstrates what can often be a problem with new technology in that it is often introduced for what may prove to be the wrong reasons. It is often sold and bought by management as a way of increasing efficiency by reducing direct labour costs. Certainly this was encouraged in this case by the holding company's requirement of a two-year payback period for capital investments which encourages a short-term cost-saving approach. Clearly, if savings are ultimately achieved this may help to make the company's products more price competitive. However, if as frequently occurs in todays market conditions, flexibility, quality and speed of delivery are equally important criteria for success, this needs to be reflected in the design of the manufacturing and delivery system.

As was demonstrated in the FMS case, it is possible to design a system that is both flexible and efficient, although this may have implications for the relative roles and disposition of the people and technology. It is therefore arguable in this case that had the company thought through the relationship of the new system to their strategic objectives, a different model and concept for the paint spraying process might have been devised. Such a system should have provided greater flexibility of response from both the technology and the people concerned.

8.3 Technological determinism

The second major issue raised by this case relates to the dominance of technology and technological considerations particularly during the planning process. In this instance, although the company stated that it was largely for 'insurance' purposes, heavy reliance was placed on external technical consultants and contractors.

Interviews with the consultants who were experienced in this type of application indicated that they considered this to be a relatively straightforward job. They also said that they considered that any manpower or trade union considerations were internal matters to be dealt with by management and were not their concern. Indeed, they expressed surprise that there had not been more resistance or problems with the shop floor over the impending introduction of the robot and new system.

Despite the researcher sitting in on some of the planning meetings and, intervening on such questions as training and work organisation in practice, the process was almost entirely dominated by considerations of technical and task factors (see Figure 8.1). Questions on training and work organisation were dismissed in a matter of moments and as none of the staff, with the exception of the supervisor, were involved, concern about these issues appeared to be secondary.

The apparent lack of concern or interest in these issues may have been reinforced by several factors:

❏   The engineering background and assumptions by the majority of people in the planning team; not only the contractors and consultants but also the members of the management team.

❏   The fact that in comparison to the technology and the unknowns involved, manpower and industrial issues were thought to be simple and relatively unproblematic.

❑ The lack of a vigorous trade union organisation and representation may have meant that management considered the workforce to be a relatively 'soft touch'. Their relative lack of knowledge and militancy meant that they did not make any particular demands and were likely to acquiesce in whatever solutions were proposed.

❑ The belief by management that they had done their job by the workforce in that they had communicated over a long period of time what their intentions were and in broad terms what the new system involved. In this they may, either by accident or design, have confused the needs of communication with those of consultation on a change of this magnitude.

Hence, the result of this technical domination in the planning process meant that issues such as job satisfaction and motivation, work organisation, communication, and supervision and management of the new system was given little consideration. The changes that might be required to the organisational and human variables were not recognised and this only came to light after the event rather than during the planning phase. This feature and the dominance of technical consideration during the planning phase seem to be characteristic of many applications. As is illustrated in Figure 8.1, the human and organisational issues often only emerge after the event when it may be more difficult to make the necessary changes.

Figure 8.1   Phases in planning technological changes

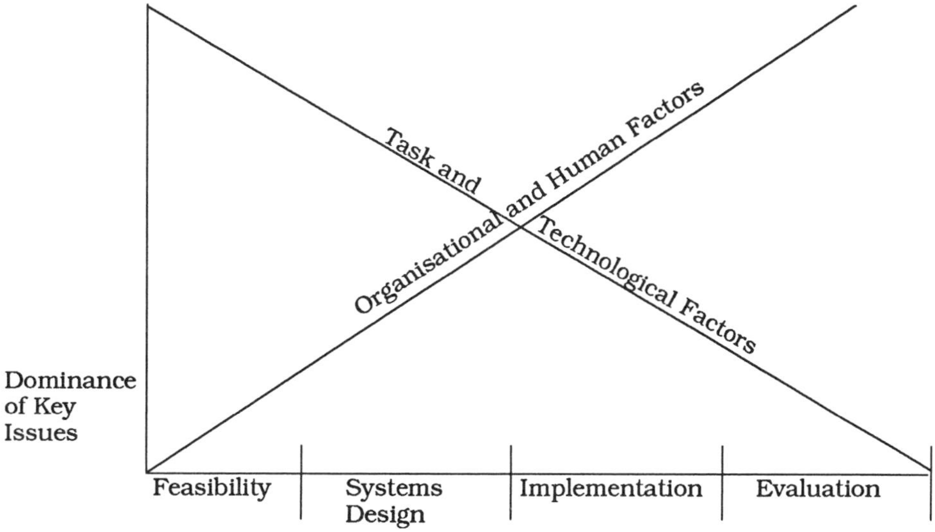

8.4 Impact of automation and job satisfaction

The question also arises from the case as to why people were so disillusioned with the new system and dissatisfied with their jobs. In this instance it proved possible to use before-and-after studies of people's reactions to the job characteristics using the Hackman and Oldham questionnaire and follow-up discussions.

In the first instance management had made assumptions about the paint sprayers' attitudes to their jobs. This influenced their approach to the introduction of the new system, but was subsequently shown to be ill founded. Management assumed that the paint sprayers found the hand spraying job relatively undemanding and that they would welcome the new system for the improvements in hygiene and working conditions that it would afford. However, analysis of their reactions to the job of manual paint spraying showed that sprayers derived a considerable amount of satisfaction from what they regarded as a manually skilled and responsible job.

Job Design theory would argue that for motivation and job satisfaction any individual or team should have

i.   A clear and meaningful goal
ii.   Discretion and responsibility to plan and organise their own work
iii. Direct and meaningful feedback on their achievement.

With individual paint spraying these conditions were largely satisfied in that the workforce knew clearly what they had to achieve in terms of performance and quality standard. They had discretion to choose in what order to spray the components and how to achieve the desired results, and from their own efforts and feedback and from the inspection function they knew whether they were achieving the desired results or not.

However, the automation of the process changed all this in that as individual operators, performing only one part of the total process, their sense of involvement in the whole task and on task identity dropped dramatically from 4.8 to 2.2 on the Hackman and Oldham scale (see Figure 7.3).

Similarly, regarding variety, whereas previously they used a variety of skills and actions and worked on a variety of components, they were now confined (partly by their own choice) to a single, narrowly defined, repetitive task, eg putting on or taking off components from the track. Thus the score on variety had fallen from 4.2 to 2.1.

The scores on autonomy also dropped significantly from 4.8 to 3.1 in that they no longer had any discretion about which jobs or components to work on and feedback fell from 5.3 to 2.8 because only the person at the end of the line saw the results and the final product.

Although the jobs previously were individual jobs the people were able to communicate and interact with one another, the supervisor, the inspector, and the degreaser. Now, with the physical distance between individual operators and the automated nature of the process their score for dealing with others dropped from 3.2 to 1.1. Add to this the fact that there were continuing problems with drifting paint, excessive heat and a robot that more often than not didn't work, the group and their supervisor experienced feelings of profound disillusionment and dissatisfaction. Whereas previously they had felt that they were doing an important and responsible job (as their score of 6 on Task Significance would signify) they now felt that they were just nobodies and that the robot did the job. They were simply machine minders with no sense of responsibility or involvement at all. As one member said, "It would have been better to automate the system completely rather than create such 'monkey' type, mindless, boring jobs." A comment from the supervisor graphically illustrated the point when he said "people are now saying if you can piss, you can paint!

8.5 Alternative forms of work organisation

Current knowledge of alternative forms of work organisation would suggest that there were options and alternatives, the relevance of which could and perhaps should have been considered in this situation. Recognised alternative and options include:

i.   Job Rotation
ii.   Job Enlargement
iii. Job Involvement
iv.   Group Working

Management were aware of the potential problems of boredom and monotony arising from the new system and *were inclined towards a system of job rotation*' to counteract this. In the event concern with technical and production problems meant that this was never adopted or encouraged. Operators gravitated to the jobs that suited them or they disliked least but were not willing to initiate job rotation of their own volition. In fact in their minds one job was as bad as the other and so they didn't really see the point. Had job rotation been encouraged and implemented it might have helped to increase people's Task Identity scores and sense of involvement in the whole task as well as improving their scores on Variety and Feedback.

Clearly, the concepts of job enlargement (horizontal integration of tasks) and job enrichment (vertical delegation and integration of responsibility and decision making) have relevance to this situation. However, they cannot be literally applied unless one person takes responsibility for the whole process.

These approaches are relevant to the concept of group working which does provide for elements of job rotation, enlargement and enrichment. In practice, it could involve the group working as a team and taking responsibility for the overall operation of the paint spraying process. In this situation the group would operate more as a team in which each operator, although having an individual task, identifies with the process as a whole and with the objectives that the team is working towards. These objectives each include targets in terms of delivery dates to customers, output and productivity targets, quality standards and the development of the process. In these circumstances the boundaries of individual tasks become more blurred and job rotation occurs naturally as part of the overall task of getting the job done. Jobs are enlarged in the sense that people feel that they are involved in the whole process rather than on one initial task. Job enrichment occurs in that individuals, as part of the team, become involved in the planning and organisational decisions required. Closer liaison and involvement with functions such as production control, quality and maintenance also enrich the jobs and help to break down the traditional barriers that exist between these functions.

Were such an alternative to be adopted, the scores of the operators on such factors as variety, task identity and significance, autonomy and feedback would arguably be very much higher as would those of feedback from others and teamwork.

8.6 Social structure of organisations

However, perhaps the most important question arising from this case is why, when knowledge and information on job design and work organisation was available, it was not used? Why was so little attention given to the people and organisational variables and why was the available expertise not used?

Some clues have already been given to the answers to these questions in the dominance of engineering in the education, training and experience of the management and planning teams. Valuable though this is, it can create a problem when dealing with what is a multi-disciplinary type problem or development. The problem would equally arise if for example it was dominated by accountants who, while they might have a good command of the financial aspects of the change, might have difficulty in appreciating some of the technical and human considerations.

The dominance of engineering models and concepts of people and organisation are likely to condition and influence the approach adopted in the design of the new system. Engineers arguably view an organisation more as a 'mechanism' than as an 'organism', a 'closed' rather than an 'open' system. Thus people will have to fit round the technology into predetermined slots and perform precise functions rather like the mechanics of a clock. The only problem with a clock is that it has to be wound to make it go and thus supervision is required to direct, organise, motivate and control the workforce.

It may be more difficult for people with limited awareness in the social sciences to recognise the nature or existence of the informal organisation, identified as long ago as in the Hawthorne studies. In this sense the organisation can be viewed as an 'organism' whose performance and survival depends as much on the interaction between people in the system, and between it and its boundaries, as on the performance of individual tasks. In this situation individuals take much more responsibility for their own motivation and management, and the boundaries of jobs and between jobs are less rigidly defined.

These analogies apply very directly to the paint spraying case where management approach to organisation design in the first instance was one of scientific management, utilising the 'concept of a closed mechanistic system'. However experience and the problems arising from its operation increasingly suggested that a different model employing a more 'open organismic system' concept would have been more appropriate.

These observations were borne out by an analysis of system boundaries in the change from the manual to the automated system. Whereas in the manual system (see Figure7.1) there was a coincidence between the task and job boundaries in the sense that each individual paint sprayer had the information, discretion and control to perform his function, the same cannot be said for the individual operators in the automated system (see Figure 7.2). Here the task of paint spraying is performed by the system as a whole, while individual operators are performing such activities as putting on and taking off components from the track. It is only by involvement at the level of the overall task that there is a coincidence of job and task boundaries. Only if each individual operator is a member of a team who are able to plan, organise and control their work and the overall process will there be a coincidence of the job and task boundaries.

8.7 Role of supervision in an automated system

Discussion on possible alternatives in terms of work organisation inevitably raises the question of the role of supervision in such a system.

In this particular case the existing supervisor in the manual system performed a traditional supervisory role scheduling and allocating work and dealing with problems across the boundary, particularly with quality, inspection and maintenance.

Clearly, if a group form of organisation were adopted many of the decisions and functions would be performed by the group members themselves, thus raising the question of whether there is a role for a supervisor in the conventional sense in an automated system such as this.

The company clearly had not recognised the change that might arise in this area because shortly after the new system had been operating the existing supervisor left. He had been initially enthusiastic about the new system but once it was operating became bored and disinterested. He tried to create interest by becoming more involved in the technical and maintenance aspects but was then disciplined for this by management who did not consider it as his job and this undoubtedly contributed to his departure.

Without any consideration as to the need or the opportunities that this might create, the company simply replaced him with a new supervisor who, by disposition, was happily more employee centred in his approach. As was discussed earlier in the case, the supervisor himself recognised the greater interdependence of jobs in the plant and encouraged a move towards greater team work and involvement. This, however, happened very much by accident rather than design, but his good intentions suffered in the prevailing climate of production and output within the firm. For example, it had been his intention to hold regular meetings of the group to help develop team work but this had not proved possible in the event and it did not appear to have been encouraged.

However, these experiences do provide clues as to the changes that may be required as a result of automation, particularly if this is accompanied by moves towards group and team working.

The supervisor in these circumstances is redundant in the conventional sense. What may be required is more of a team leader whose role involves the development of team work. Thus, such a leader may help the group in clarifying their objectives and evaluating their own performance, and may provide them with training in such functions as communication, interpersonal skills and problem solving and encourage them to act as a sort of quality circle. While initially this may be quite a full-time job, increasingly as the group's competence and confidence develops, the team leader will need to pull back to give the group the freedom of operation they need to manage themselves and their activity.

8.8 Management attitudes and values

The question still remains as to why, when information and expertise were available, these problems and needs for change to the social structure of the organisation were not recognised or predicted. If these factors were recognised why was nothing done about them?

One possible explanation is inability to apply knowledge. The Managing Director, who was responsible for overseeing the project, was himself a management student who had attended a workshop on job design and work organisation. So, although he was not involved in all the detail, he could certainly have influenced the overall approach to the design of the system and its introduction.

Moreover, as part of the Teaching Company scheme the firm had access to the Polytechnic staff and as co-ordinator of the scheme the author's own knowledge and contacts were available to them. In addition they had a full-time Teaching Company Associate resident at the firm who was aware through tutorials of the needs and opportunities in this direction.

With such resources at their disposal one must conclude that there were other factors which accounted for the approach which was adopted which relate to the relative roles of management and employees and to the management's need for control.

Conventional management theory emphasises managers' need to direct, organise, motivate and control the work force. This approach is particularly prevalent in the traditional parts of the engineering industry and may often be more readily accepted in a rural environment when traditions of 'master and servant' die hard. However, there is evidence that employees in rural areas are willing to accept more responsibility if management are prepared to give it (Turner and Lawrence, 1965). Basically, changes of the type discussed earlier involving work group autonomy and the removal of direct supervision fly in the face of strongly held notions of the conventional roles of management and work people.

Technology should if anything increase management ability to control the production process and minimise disruption by the human element. Therefore the introduction of new technology should enable management to reduce its dependence on human factors and either eliminate or reduce their influence on the production process. This notion fits with the conflict model of management where the means of production are seen as a potential source of profit and labour as an unfortunate but necessary cost. Therefore, anything that can help to reduce costs and their dependence on people will be welcomed by management. This strategy however is based on the assumptions by management that the only thing people really want from their work is money and that therefore they will do as little as possible for as much as possible in return. However, evidence from research and from the paint sprayers own reaction to their jobs is that they appreciate and respond to responsibility and involvement. Thus, given the right conditions they are capable of self-motivation, management and innovation and rather than just being a cost are capable of generating profit through improved performance, productivity, problem solving and development. Such concepts and assumptions however call for a very different approach to management and organisation than the conventional model and imply a very different approach to the introduction of new technology. A summary of these implications is included in the following chapter.

8.9 Organisational culture

Observation and analysis of this case study does appear to reinforce the relevance of the prevailing culture of the organisation to the ole and introduction of new technology.

Rightly or wrongly, this small but quite successful company does have a relatively conventional and traditional approach to the management and organisation of its workforce. The style of management, though varying from one individual to another, overall is benevolent but autocratic and paternalistic. Trade unions though recognised are not particularly well organised or militant and the level of membership is quite low. In this context while management might see the need to communicate, they would not feel any obligation to consult with either the trade unions or the shop floor. Consistent with this overall style is the notion that management are the primary sources of information and expertise and only with reluctance would admit their need for any external information or advice. Planning is seen as very much a management function and prerogative and therefore the idea of involvement of the people doing the job in the planning of change does not fit with these assumptions.

Similarly, the functions of work organisation, motivation and control are very much the 'raison d'etre' of middle management and it would be very foreign in such a culture for these functions to be delegated to the people doing the job. Indeed, as the attitudes of the paint sprayers themselves revealed they are quite accustomed to accepting management's right to make the decisions, even if in the event they don't like the results. They have not had the opportunity or the training for a wider involvement and would be inclined to the view that it is management's job to manage and that's what they are paid to do.

If this was the prevailing culture would an alternative approach have stood a chance of succeeding anyway? The changes and alternatives proposed for the organisation of the paint spraying department are in such contrast to the prevailing culture and climate of the firm that even if they had been accepted the chance of their long-term survival could arguably have been rather slim.

Of the alternatives, job rotation, which had clearly been suggested, was the one most likely to have been accepted as this would not require any changes in the organisation structure or in responsibilities and decision making. In other words it would not 'rock the boat' and while its benefits may be limited at least it might have been acceptable in the prevailing climate.

Nevertheless, the price of making change in such a culture is that people may suffer at the expense of technology. Frequently they will suffer in terms of employment and job security but equally they may suffer in terms of job satisfaction, human involvement and the quality of their working life. Such outcomes, apart from being socially undesirable, do have their costs in economic terms. The effects on attitudes, motivation, attendance to detail, stress, health and safety, and the effective utilisation of human skills and enterprise are likely to be very negative. Whether such solutions and outcomes are effective in today's competitive markets and business environment is, to say the least, questionable. Many people would argue that we can ill afford to employ people in such jobs in which we make so little demand of their potential contribution.

The final question therefore that this case study poses is whether this situation is inevitable and what possibilities exist for changing the prevailing culture?

Much of the problem seems to arise from treating the introduction of new technology as a specific change in one specific variable in the organisation, namely in terms of technology. If management recognises the need to keep all the key variables in the organisation under regular review and accepts the need for change as a continuing function of business survival and organisational effectiveness, then the adoption of new technology will be put in its proper perspective, ie it is just one aspect of the continuing changes required for effectiveness in today's business environment.

While we cannot expect technology to change the world , the scale and scope of the changes involved does provide the opportunity for some fundamental questions to be asked. It can, as discussed in the earlier cases in Part II, provide an opportunity to unfreeze existing attitudes not only amongst management but amongst the workforce as well.

If we add to this the need for organisations to be open to information, experience and knowledge from outside then they may be encouraged to explore and experiment with alternative approaches and to learn from the process.

The Teaching Company schemes in which the firm participated were funded by the Science and Engineering Research Council and thus the expectations of all concerned were for technical change and development. Subsequently the SERC and Economic and Social Science Research Council have combined and also become involved with the Teaching Company scheme and although joint funding of projects is still the exception rather than the rule more mutual influence will hopefully take place.

However, while there might have been problems in bringing about a change in culture in this specific situation, evidence from the case studies in Part IV provides illustrations and encouragement of what it is possible to achieve.

9 COMPUTERISATION OF AN ORDER OFFICE - A CASE STUDY IN OFFICE AUTOMATION

9.1 Background to the company

From the outset of this research it had been a matter of concern to include office applications of new technology as much as manufacturing applications. The opportunity to study the computerisation of an office came as a result of the author's involvement with a brewery, who were part of a large national group.

The company, which had been concerned about the impact of the Bullock report, which advocated employee and trade union representation on the boards of companies, contacted the author to help them try to develop employee involvement at the level of their jobs.

Following a management survey into their interpretation of employee involvement a working party was established from which a number of initiatives and changes stemmed. In particular, problems had become apparent with the distribution function which proved to be inefficient and costly. Also people felt that the draymen lacked motivation and that there was a big divide between them and the staff in the order office and load planning.

As a result of consultation with trade and trade union representatives it was agreed to restructure the organisation into smaller teams of draymen, load planners and operators, each serving regular customers in geographical areas called 'zones'.

The author's role was more a catalyst than as a prescriptive consultant helping the organisation to define its goals and measure where it stood in relation to these. Informally in the planning meetings, options and alternatives were discussed to obtaining greater involvement but it was up to the individual departmental managers to determine their new strategy.

Following the change in the distribution organisation, it proved possible to conduct a thorough evaluation of change which proved that it had been very successful. Considerable improvements were achieved in customer service, cost reduction, job satisfaction, teamwork and industrial relations (Bailey 1983). The Distribution Manager won the National Distribution Manager Award for the year in question and this was well publicised within the company and was felt would serve as encouragement to other functions to plan their own changes.

Following this, when no longer employed by the company the author took groups of students to see the distribution function as an example of what could be achieved. It was on one of these visits that we learnt of the company's intention to computerise the system. Having expressed interest in this development the opportunity was sought to be involved. Although not asked for professional advice, it was possible to negotiate an opportunity to review the changes particularly regarding their effects on the job of the staff concerned.

From previous involvement with the company it was not difficult to arrange for interviews and data collection on the system and its effects. In fact people were only to ready to talk about them.

In the first instance, interviews were held with the new Distribution Manager to obtain background about the changes and what the company were trying to achieve. Interviews were also held with the Manager in charge of Transport and Warehousing and the newly appointed Telesales Supervisor to get more details of the system and their approach adopted to its introduction.

Some time was also spent with the telesales girls and the load planner to study the new system and its operation. From previous work and data from the Hackman and Oldham survey on the manual system it was possible to obtain comparative data by issuing the survey to the telesales staff. Following this, interviews were held with the staff to discuss their reactions to the new system and the effects on their job satisfaction. Apart from this, informal discussions were held with the Manager and Telesales Supervisor and these occasions provided invaluable opportunity to obtain informal feedback about the new organisation and the system involved.

9.2 The new system

The new system, based on a Data General MV 4000, provides the operator with the following functions:

1. Order taking - the details of customers' orders are entered onto keyboard

2. Load planning - the operator records delivery note number and enters it onprogramme

3. Delivery confirmation - confirmation of exact deliveries made on corrected delivery note

4. Post delivery order entry - key orders back in

5. Stock recording - records changes in stock levels on continuing basis.

Each telesales operator had their own VDU screen and a list of customers with basic data about address and telephone number. Three operators were also provided with the customer order history for the previous five weeks, thus enabling them to check the customer's current level of stocks and what additional potential orders they may require. Orders when received were immediately keyed into the system and printed out on a delivery note in load planning.

The system was developed centrally at the head office as a package to be used throughout the group. There was little, if any, adaptation of the system to suit local circumstances and as the customer manager said, *"we had to make the package work for us"*. Experience showed that there was a number of facilities that would have been helpful at the local level, but all of the development work was done at the head office and there were no facilities for providing a local input in the system design.

9.3 Reorganisation of the department

At about the same time the new Distribution Manager felt the need to rationalise the distribution department in order to counteract rising costs and offer a more efficient delivery service. As with computerisation, the aim of the rationalisation of the distribution department was to reduce costs while maintaining the level of service to the customer.

The concept of zones was abandoned on the grounds that it led to inflexibility of labour and unequal work load between zones.

Depots cost money in terms of wages and stocks and the nine depots in the region were reduced to four hich, it was felt, would ease stock control. Now articulated lorries have to serve the three regional depots.

The number of draymen was reduced from 64 to 41, eliminating the third man and employing a larger vehicle with a capacity of nine tons. Originally, there were four load planners, one to each zone. They have now been reduced from four to one, the latter being in control of the whole area, thus it was felt improving flexibility.

As regards the telesales operators, the previous structure meant that they each dealt with any of a number of promotions or types of sales activity. This, it was felt, led to inefficiency and people making mistakes. Now the full-time telesales staff have been replaced by part-timers who, by working in the morning, are able to get all the orders in before lunch. This helps the load planners by making all the afternoon available to plan the following day's deliveries.

A working party was set up for the reorganisation and since then Saturday morning problem solving sessions have been introduced with the draymen. Distribution management felt that the involvement of people in target setting, decision making and feedback on achievement and how well they have done has paid off.

9.4 Introduction of new system

Initially, people lacked confidence in the equipment. Down time could be anything from five minutes to five hours and this tended to undermine morale and confidence. However, training sessions on the new equipment of about 2 or 3 hours were set up alongside manual operations. Discussions took place on progress and problems with the intention of keeping a relaxed atmosphere.

Discussions took place with the staff about the changes required. One of the load planners was transferred to be checker and another left the company, but only after training had been given to her on VDU operation to help her get another job.

Once the new system was installed, new job descriptions were created raising the jobs from Staff Grade 2 to 3. Although a number of new staff were appointed, the higher grade compensated to some extent for reduced hours involved in going from full-time to part-time work.

The two systems were operated side by side for 7 weeks during which time specialised training was provided by the head office staff in operating the new system, eg cancelling and amending orders.

Evening sessions were held each week to de-bug the system. Managers would phone in orders presenting the girls with types of problems anticipated. Then the operators were put for a whole day into an existing live system within the group and this helped overcome nervousness about the first day' operation of the new system.

The system was eventually launched, with champagne and buffet lunch, to mark the degree of involvement of everyone from the managing director to the draymen in the introduction of the new system. Full-time staff, who were unable to accept the change to part-time employment, were offered training and assistance to find alternative full-time work.

9.5 Role of supervisor

The appointment of a telesales supervisor was intended to shield the girls from problems and queries which might interfere with the basic task of order taking. Whereas previously the girls handled their own problems and queries these were now referred to the supervisor. Problems such as complaints on delivery and queries on paper work are dealt with by the supervisor who adopts the policy that 'the buck stops here'.

Another key role played by the supervisor was in terms of training. Product training was being organised to keep staff up to date with special promotions and a monthly training session was held in the evenings to iron out problems.

9.6 Results

1.   Costs

Considerable savings were achieved in terms of reduced costs, by reducing the number of depots from nine to four, the number of draymen from 64 to 41 and the number of vehicles as a result of introducing larger vehicles.

2. Customer service

Customer service with the zoning system was very high, approaching 100% deliveries on the next day.

Job satisfaction and involvement

Although data was obtained from the staff both before and after the change, in the elapsed period some members of the group had changed. Therefore one cannot be sure that observed differences were entirely due to the changes in the jobs. However analysis of the two sets of Hackman and Oldham data indicates that while the general level of satisfaction of the telesales staff with their jobs was quite high, there were quite significant differences in the key characteristics of their jobs under the new system from those under the zoning system. In analysing this, one must allow for the fact that the new incumbents were part-time as opposed to full-time employees and that this possibly leads to different expectations of their work. Generally, they felt satisfied with their jobs because they fitted in easily with school hours and home commitments and the level of pay is high.

Variety

As can be seen from Figure 9.1 variety decreased considerably in comparison to the zoning system, where the telesales girls could, for example, be involved in load planning. While the introduction of products and promotions has increased their feeling of variety over the original structure, there was a decline in this aspect of the job.

Task identity

Of more significance, however, is people's assessment of task identity which declined from 5.5 to 2.3. Previously, staff involved in this function felt involved in the total delivery tasks, whereas now they performed only one part of it, albeit a very important part in their eyes, as the score on task significance indicates.

Autonomy

The other factor which declined is autonomy where the increased involvement of the supervisor with complaints and problem solving, and the fact that calls they had to make were predetermined, left the girls little discretion in how they did their work.

Feedback

With introduction of zoning, feedback from the customer to telesales was vastly improved because of the direct contact with their own set of customers. Under the new system, although they don't deal with any particular customers, they still rated this factor quite highly, although they didn't know what happens to a load after it leaves and they didn't see the delivery confirmation.

Social factors
As can be seen from Figure 9.1 there was some deterioration of feedback from others, ie colleagues and/or supervisors, and also on dealing with others, either clients or colleagues. How much of this was due to the introduction of the computer as such, or to the change in work organisation, is questionable. Certainly the girls felt that they got less feedback on their own performance from the supervisor in the new situation than before. As they were working individually there was also less opportunity for feedback from colleagues on telesales or load planning.

Figure 9.1   Characteristics of telephone sales operators' jobs as a result of changes in organisation and computerisation

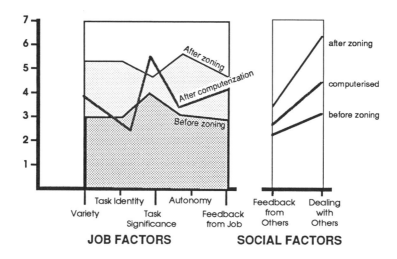

Similarly, while they rated their customer contact through the telephone quite highly, the relative lack of contact with load planning and the draymen led to a decline in their assessment of dealing with others.

Although the assumption could be made that, as part-timers with relatively good pay and convenient hours, job satisfaction for the telesales staff was not important, evidence from the survey would not support this assumption. The general level of expectation of interest and satisfaction was quite high. The results of the survey showed an average measure of 5.2 on a 1-7 point scale, measuring the growth needs of the staff. This meant that a number of people found the work rather tedious and monotonous and this they felt did affect their motivation to the job.

10 ANALYSIS OF OFFICE AUTOMATION CASE

Clearly, the major questions raised by the case are the effect on the organisation of work: whether or not other alternatives or options could have been adopted at the time the system was introduced; what changes might currently be possible to improve the characteristics of the jobs; and how far the existing technical system inhibited any changes in work organisation or job design.

Copies of a version of the paper were made available to the company and the Distribution Director at the time. Although there was no formal response or comments from the company to the issues and questions posed, informally concern was expressed by middle management and employees over the changes that had occurred. These basically centred around the loss of communication and contact between the staff involved, namely telesales, load planners and the draymen, and between the staff and customers. There was a strong feeling that what had been achieved in terms of reduced costs was at the expense of staff motivation and involvement and of service to the customer. It was felt that there had been a major shift within the firm towards a policy of 'hard sell' and cost reduction. The opinion was that although staff had no option but to go along with this, they didn't really believe in it.

10.1 Harmonisation and integration
One of the most interesting questions in the introduction of new technology is whether the issues raised and potential solutions apply equally to white collar/office situations as they do to manufacturing and the shop floor, and further, how far such divisions have any logic or make any sense in today's computerised settings.

In the previous reorganisation the draymen had been brought much closer to the office staff by creating small integrated teams who were involved in the whole delivery process. This not only helped to reduce costs and improve the delivery service, but it helped to remove the us and them situation and the divide between the office and the yard.

The introduction of computerised systems of management and information can potentially do much to integrate previously separate functions by providing a common database. There was the opportunity and potential here to further integrate and enhance team work to the benefit of both customers and the staff. However, the approach adopted was one of 'scientific management' in that the separate functions of telesales, local planning and delivery were emphasised. In the original zoning structure it was recognised that the task was the 'delivery' of the beers and that this depended on co-operation and teamwork between those that received the orders, those that planned the loads and those that delivered the beers. The task boundary was around 'those needed to work together to get the customer the produce and service they required'. The teams that had been created to such good effect were broken up (a la Durham Coal Mines) to meet the perceived needs of increased efficiency and to fit the design of the new computer system.

Human contact and interaction was largely replaced by technology and the computer to the potential detriment of relationships not only between members of staff, but also potentially with the customer.

10.2 Changes in business environment and managerial strategy

This case study graphically illustrates two alternative strategies to improving organisational effectiveness on the one hand through people and, on the other, through technology. It demonstrates the advantages and benefits from each, but it also illustrates the limitations of over dependence on either strategy. In what was a self-evident and classic illustration of a socio-technical system, the strategy swung dramatically from a social to a technical solution of the problem (see Figure 10.1).

In the one case, emphasis on people, flexibility, teamwork, involvement and communication was seen as the best strategy, while in the other emphasis was on specialisation of tasks, technology and managerial control. As suggested in Figure 10.2, socio-technical system theory would suggest that the more effective strategy is a design solution which integrates both people and technology in the achievement of the task.

Figure 10.1   Alternative models of systems design

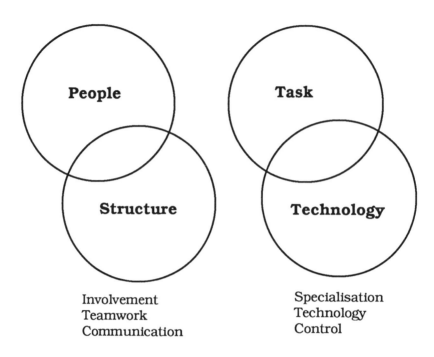

Involvement
Teamwork
Communication

Specialisation
Technology
Control

Figure 10.2   Total systems design and integration

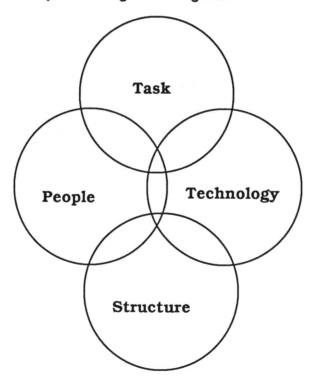

10.3   The social solution

The original change to the zoning structure took place in a climate of increasing emphasis on employee participation. Indeed the overall culture within the brewery was one of employee involvement. This helped to provide an umbrella within which the involvement project was initiated.

Following a survey at management level their definition of employee involvement was defined as:

❑   greater job satisfaction and team work leading to a better service to the customer and increased profitability.

With the overall objectives established individual managers and functions were encouraged to evaluate their situation and that of their own departments. A management working party was formed and many changes took place. However, in particular there had been criticism of the performance of distribution and the manager concerned responded to the challenge by initiating a major reorganisation of the distribution function to better achieve these objectives.

His approach to the problem was highly participative, involving consultation with representatives of both customers and staff. The trade representatives, who came after the draymen, were brought in at the outset and involved in the analysis of the problem.

However, they were also able to identify a model which they would hope to replicate in any solution that was developed. In this instance the problems experienced in the larger department at the head office contrasted with the smaller rural depots where motivation, team work and customer service seemed to be very effective. This use of a model (a concept of the situation that ideally should apply) appears to be very useful in helping people develop a solution in practice.

Following these discussions agreement was reached to restructure the distribution organisation around the concept of smaller autonomous units, similar to the rural depots in which the function of telesales, load planning and delivery were combined into closely integrated teams. This combined with the ability to serve a regular set of customers led to quite dramatic improvements in motivation, teamwork, efficiency, customer service and industrial relations.

Continued contact with the organisation made it possible to follow up the results of the change, and to conduct a thorough evaluation. In addition, the project which was quite widely publicised was selected as the winning entry to the annual National Distribution Management competition and the distribution manager won the award. However, it is indicative of his style and approach that he took the trade representatives with him to receive the award, because he argued that their success was as much a result of their efforts as of his.

Referring to Figure 10.2, the strategy adopted, ie a people-centred participative approach, profoundly influenced the design solutions and the resultant organisational structure and management style. It placed an emphasis on the notion of employee, involvement, motivation, delegation, autonomy and team work and placed a high premium on the need for good communications and relationships. In short, it was a classic human relations approach with all the emphasis on the social side of the socio-technical systems equation.

10.4   The technical solution
However, technology in the zoning system was very basic, involving manual records and customer plates with customer records and delivery information. These had to be manually maintained and up-dated and were no doubt by today's standards very inefficient. Also, as described in the case, whereas the late 70s was a period of growth and expansion, the early 80s saw a decline in economic activity and stabilisation of beer sales although costs and competition continued to increase.

The business environment in which the firm was operating therefore changed and this was reflected in a change of climate and of management within distribution. A new director and distribution manager were appointed with experience of new, more efficient distribution systems. These systems which involved trunkers with detachable trailers and containers meant that the firm could dramatically reduce the number of depots by holding stock locally overnight to be picked up for local deliveries in the morning. Similarly, changes to the manning levels of drays were negotiated from three man to two man crews which achieved further savings.

At the same time, with the competition to retain market share, there was increasing emphasis on sales rather than marketing or customer service and in the role of telephone selling in achieving orders. This coincided with the development centrally of a new computerised sales order processing system which was intended to provide more efficient backup and information systems to enhance telesales and delivery performance. The system also provided information for load planning and for confirmation of deliveries. Thus, as can be seen, there was a quite dramatic change in the climate in which distribution management were operating and in their interpretation of what were the criteria for effectiveness and for survival in a very competitive environment.

Perhaps, rightly, the strategy employed was one of rationalisation, consolidation and automation all with the primary aim of reducing costs and increasing sales. Service, though important, was not thought to be the predominant factor for success and the effects of the changed strategy were reflected throughout the reorganisation that took place.

In the first instance the sales order processing system which was developed centrally was orientated around the role of the telesales operator. As was described in the case study, it is designed in order to help them increase their customer calling rate and to provide a better technique in terms of customer information. In this respect it is very effective in that information on customer past orders enabled the operator to be much more sensitive to likely customer needs.

However, the system was clearly designed with certain assumptions about the role of the staff associated with the system, their relation with one another and on the management structures concerned. The telesales operators were now confined to a predetermined and repetitive sales and order taking function with little if any involvement with the other aspects of the delivery tasks. Their discretion and involvement in solving problems have been removed in that a telesales supervisor has been appointed who takes over any queries or problems that need to be resolved. Their links with particular customers have been severed and they now specialise in the promotion of particular products. The implication of this is that it was felt to be more important that they were familiar with particular products than with particular customers as in the past.

Similarly, the links with load planning and the draymen have been broken in that the load planner was now physically separate and some distance from the telesales office and the draymen do not relate to any particular telesales operator. The zone structure as already indicated was abandoned in the interests of greater flexibility and utilisation of resources.

Thus the structure and approach to management and organisation in distribution as a result of these changes was therefore very much one of 'scientific management' employing specialisation of function and hierarchical control. Motivation is largely by financial incentives and co-ordination is provided by management. Technology is employed to help increase output and productivity, communication is primarily by telecommunications and the data provided by the computer.

Clearly, in the design of the computer system little account had been taken of the existing social structures in the department and of the significance of the zone organisation. If these factors were considered it would appear that it was based on the assumptions of separate functions. No provision was made in the design of the system for information of deliveries made to be provided for the telesales girls. Thus, one of the most important job design criteria, namely feedback, was not catered for and this could have important implications for their motivation to achieve the sales required.

Similarly, the load planner who now performed an individual task was very isolated in a separate office, having relatively little contact with anybody other than via the computer. As a consequence, not surprisingly, his motivation and morale were rock bottom.

Rightly or wrongly therefore, the case demonstrates the impact of the technical solution on structure and style of management adopted (see Figure 10.1). As it indicates human considerations of factors such as motivation, teamwork relationships and communications did not receive much consideration. The structure and style of management was based on achieving increased efficiency through specialisation, co-ordination and control which was reinforced by the computer technology. The resultant jobs were specialised and repetitive with little human contact and much of the satisfaction, involvement and teamwork previously established was lost. Staff tended to view their jobs as purely instrumental, looking to incentives, attributed to particular promotions as a means of motivation and reward.

10.5 Questions and issues arising from the case

The issues and questions that this case study raises are in many senses very similar to those relating to the Robot Paint Spraying case:

1. How far was the approach adopted the only possible solution and what alternatives could have applied?

2. Were the results in terms of people's involvement and satisfaction inevitable, or could a better match between people and technology have been found?

3. Were the benefits in terms of increased efficiency at the possible expense of customer service and the longer term image and relationship of the firm with its customers?

4. How far, for example, in a service function such as this is it important to maintain the involvement and commitment of the staff.

Prior to the zoning project, there were many complaints about the level of customer service from the firm. Indeed it was quoted that if on a Friday night a publican rang the order office to find out what had happened to his beer, the impression given was that the girls neither knew nor cared. There is a danger that in the new system, where all the emphasis is on sales and orders and the computer makes no provision for confirmation of delivery of the order, that if staff are not motivated and responsible that a similar situation could arise again.

In a function such as this, successful completion of the TASK, namely supplying the customer with beer, is dependent not just on telesales, but also on the other people within distribution and their ability to work together to get the customer his beer. In this sense, therefore, the computer system should clearly have been designed to support not only the individuals in accomplishing their job, but also the team in successfully fulfilling the TASK. Thus, arguably the system could have been designed to provide the team with the data it needs to do the job, namely in sales, load planning and delivery information to all the members of the team and the provision of an efficient and prompt sales and delivery service. Opportunities for extra sales and for easing deliveries can be identified and problems solved. The draymen themselves can help to identify sales opportunities and how route and load planning can be improved and the telesales girls can often help to get the customer the beer he needs more quickly through their knowledge of the delivery situation.

Involvement of the staff in this type of problem solving and performance improvement could avoid the necessity and cost of a telesales supervisor and could do much to enhance the motivation, satisfaction and a sense of responsibility of the telesales girls and other members of the team.

In this situation the teams would all share the same objectives in terms of sales, costs and delivery performance, and all would receive direct and meaningful feedback on their performance against their objectives. The team, however, would have a high level of autonomy to plan and organise their work and the delivery of the beer. The computer system would enhance the provision of information to the team and feedback on the key variables concerned.

In these circumstances the scores on such factors as variety, task identity, autonomy and feedback would be much higher as would those for feedback from others and team work.

The problem here is that the computer system was developed without recognition of the existing organisation structures and without any real consultation with either local management or staff. The system was developed by the computer department in London and little account seems to have been taken of the local and human factors involved.

Whilst savings in terms of costs and increased efficiency were undoubtedly achieved, the longer term effects on customer relations and customer service are more difficult to estimate. At the time the new system was introduced, the company stated that the 'customers have not suffered'. However, customer relationships are at least in part a function of the attitudes and motivation of the staff and their willingness to help and serve the customer. If, as a result of rationalisation and technological change, people's satisfaction and sense of involvement suffer, this may ultimately affect their attitudes to their jobs and to the customers. In a competitive climate, unless they are a 'tied property' the customers have the freedom to take their business elsewhere.

11 OBSERVATIONS AND CONCLUSIONS ON PART III

Whilst our objective at this stage of the investigation was to see how job design concepts would be used in the introduction of new technology, the results of our investigations reveal why they are not. In both the cases examined the companies were aware of job design concepts and had access to job design information and expertise. However, despite being offered these facilities, their priorities and concerns were in different directions. Neither company seemed to have learned from their previous experience of these issues and preoccupation with economic and technical issues seemed to virtually rule out human and social considerations.

In both cases alternative forms of management and work organisation could have improved the fit between human and technical needs, but the opportunity to achieve this was not taken. Our analysis of the reasons for this suggest that this was not due to lack of knowledge or that the alternatives were not feasible. The reasons were more to do with the assumptions held by management about the relative roles of people and technology and what they thought would be effective in the situation concerned.

Whereas the two cases in the first stage of our investigation served as something of a revelation of what was possible, the next two cases showed what was not. They represent something of a watershed in the investigation and help us to recognise the importance of such factors as strategy and culture in influencing the role of new technology and the use of job design in its introduction.

In terms of strategy the cases demonstrate that if management see their objectives largely in terms of achieving cost reduction through new technology, this will have inevitable consequences on the role and contribution of people in the process. In these circumstances, as the two case studies highlight, job satisfaction and employee involvement are likely to suffer. While this may be undesirable from a human point of view, the question also arises as to whether in today's circumstances these are the right objectives to pursue. At a time when other criteria such as quality, customer services and corporate image are also important factors in achieving business success, a strategy which minimises the people and their involvement may be questionable. Certainly there was some evidence to suggest that the companies concerned had not adequately thought out the relationship between technology and business strategy and that this had far reaching effects on the solution adopted.

However the two cases also demonstrate the significance of the prevailing culture both in influencing management's interpretation of their strategy and the means by which this can be achieved. In both cases it appeared that the culture and climate of the organisation was dominated largely by economic and technical considerations and a belief that it was management's job to manage. In these circumstances technology will again be seen as a means of minimising the human contribution and enabling management to exert more effective control over people and the performance of the system. Even if job design concepts and alternative forms of work organisation were theoretically possible and could result in a better match between people's needs and those of the organisation and the technology, it was unlikely that these would be acceptable with the culture that prevailed.

At the end of the second stage of the investigation we can now summarise some of the key factors and issues that relate to the introduction of new technology. These form a framework for our investigations during the final phase of the research.

11.1   Corporate strategy
In both cases there was a demonstrable need for the company to relate the introduction of new technology to the strategic objectives and development of the firm. There is a danger of sub-optimisation of goals in seeking cost savings through the introduction of new technology which may run counter to other longer term objectives such as the quality of service to the customer. Clarification of the strategic objectives of the business and the contribution that new technology can make to their achievement will obviously greatly influence the way it is introduced and the ultimate role played by technology.

11.2   Company philosophy

It is helpful for management to be conscious and aware of its own philosophy and the values and principles it stands for. Although there is a need for organisations to adapt and change in response to the environment, the fact that they believe in and stand by the concepts of customer service, quality, involvement of people and for example the pursuit of excellence can help to guide all those involved in and with the business and in the introduction of any change. In the cases concerned there was some evidence that these issues may have not been fully thought through and that company policy was being blown by the wind! One of the advantages of a manual system, whether in the office or on the shop floor, is that it is infinitely flexible. Once one has made the investment in the technology and its particular disposition it is much more difficult to change. In this sense the systems and solutions that are developed for today may not be appropriate for the circumstances required of tomorrow.

11.3   Technological determinism

In both cases the system was developed largely from a technical perspective with very little input or influence from the user and the people who would ultimately be involved. As a consequence the requirements of the technology dictated the requirements of the social structure rather than the reverse and people had to fit and adapt to the system.

This appears to be largely due to the composition and backgrounds of those involved in the planning and design process. The problem is that only one of the key variables, ie the needs and opportunity for change in TECHNOLOGY, is being considered (see Figure 10.2). If there had been recognition of the need to review the role and interdependence of all the key variables against the objectives the organisation was trying to achieve then different design solutions might have emerged.

11.4   People and technology

The approach adopted in both these cases implies certain assumptions about the relative role of people and technology. The implication is that people are less dependable and valuable than the technology which by contrast is predictable and controllable. The implied assumptions are that people view their work as instrumental; a necessity in order to earn the money they require to live. However, research and evidence from both these cases reveals that people are often looking for much more from their work and the chance to take responsibility and be involved.

109

Therefore, rather than diminishing the human contribution, as was done in both these cases, new systems should perhaps be designed in such a way as to enhance the contribution that people can make to improve output, productivity, quality, customer service and profit. Perhaps we should view people not just as a cost but like technology as an investment in improved performance, profit and innovation. If so this will clearly influence the relative roles of people and technology in the design of these new systems.

11.5   Design of jobs and work organisation

In both cases there is evidence of a lack of awareness or concern about the quality of the work that will result from these new systems and the contribution that job design and alternative forms of work organisation could make in these situations. Despite exposure of the organisations concerned to information, expertise and advice in these respects was not used for one reason or another. Yet analysis of both cases demonstrates that job design and alternative forms of work organisation could have helped achieve a more satisfactory match between the needs of the people concerned and the organisations and that this may well have helped increase the benefits from the new systems and the service provided to customers concerned.

11.6   Bridging the gap

Analysis of both cases shows the opportunities that new technology can create for bridging the gaps and divisions that have hampered organisations in the past. The opportunity exists for white and blue collar workers to work together and co-operate under the same physical and employment conditions. The computerised systems can also help to break down functional barriers and to give the people doing the job more involvement in the specialised functions designed to support their activities.

Finally, the opportunity exists to close gaps between management and work people by removing supervision and by involving the workforce in the management process. In neither case were these opportunities taken, but subsequent analysis of these cases shows the potential for change that new technology can create.

11.7   Models of management and organisation

The cases studied demonstrate that in many instances people are still working with conventional models and notions of management and organisation when introducing new technology. Assumptions about the role of management to provide direction and control, and of traditional structures involving specialisation and centralisation of control, profoundly influence the design of the social structures when introducing these new systems. Yet the scope and scale of technological change may provide the opportunity and need for new models and forms of management and organisation if full benefit from the technology and the people concerned is to be obtained.

These ideas and the form that an alternative model of management and organisation might take are explored in the following chapter.

12 ORGANISATION AND MANAGEMENT IN A TECHNOLOGICAL AGE

Innovations in new technology have brought far reaching changes to the technical design of office and manufacturing systems. Does new technology and computer aided systems of automation create a requirement for social innovations in terms of new models of management and organisation?

Although the examples are related, in the main, to the manufacturing situation, the issues and principles that emerge apply equally to the office setting.

12.1 Changing environment of manufacturing

Traditional structures based on specialisation of task and hierarchical management and decision making may be increasingly inappropriate to these new systems and the changing external environments in which they operate.

In the past, the market need has been for relatively long runs of standardised production, where the key factor has been high output at low cost. To meet this prescribed and predictable requirement, a 'mechanistic' type of production system capitalising on economies of scale and utilising the principles of specialisation to increase efficiency and output, may have been appropriate. Specialisation in terms of tasks, eg machinists, inspectors, maintenance personnel and planners, it was argued, helped people become proficient in these activities and increased the efficiency of the line. Similarly, decisions would be made at different levels in the hierarchy from leading hand, supervisor, management or superintendent level and by different functions, eg planning, quality control and engineering maintenance (see Figure 12.1).

However, in today's circumstances, the market increasingly requires not only low cost, but also choice and flexibility in terms of design, quality and speed of delivery. In a market where the consumer has a far greater range of products and services to choose from, the supplier must be far more customer orientated and be prepared to adapt product and production schedules to meet customer need, while still keeping costs down.

Figure 12.1 Traditional production organisation based on specialisation of functions and decision making

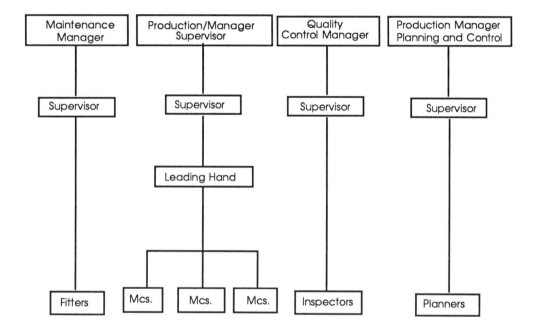

12.2 Computer based automation

It is here that the relevance and logic of computer based systems of automation and information become apparent. It is the facility to rapidly re-programme the schedules and outputs of any system, at low cost, to meet rapidly changing needs that is their 'raison d'etre'.

Such systems where properly conceived, rather than resembling the mechanistic structure of a traditional assembly line, more closely resemble a process plant such as is found in the chemical, drink or food processing industries. In these industries there has been a greater recognition of the changes to the work and skill content of jobs associated with these plants and the requirement for a delegated and decentralised style and structure of management at the operational level.

12.3 Implications for organisation

The newer, flexible, computer automated systems of manufacture call for different concepts of organisation to be applied to ensure an effective match between the people, the technology and the other variables concerned.

As can be seen in Figure 12.2 changes in the TASK (ie response of production system to market environment) and changes in TECHNOLOGY (ie technical system for creating product/service response) will require corresponding changes to STRUCTURE (ie roles and relationships) and from the PEOPLE (ie in terms of knowledge, skills and attitudes required).

Figure 12.2 Changing factors in manufacturing technology

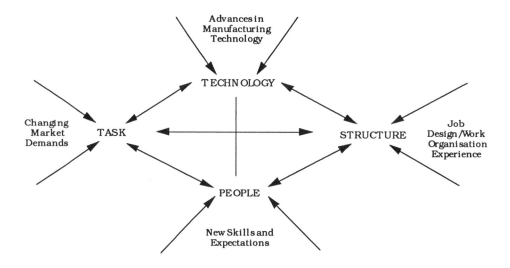

In the current decade, as opposed to the 60's and early 70's, the major forces for change are affecting the TASK variable from the market in terms of competition, and TECHNOLOGY as a result of innovations in microelectronic design. These processes increasingly demand a response in terms of the other two variables, namely PEOPLE on the one hand and STRUCTURE on the other. However, these changes in TECHNOLOGY represent something of a 'stepped' change and as a result have potentially significant destabilising effects on the other variables. Thus, potentially, as a result of planned technological change, existing attitudes and assumptions as to the role and contribution of PEOPLE and the STRUCTURES of work and relationships required may become unfrozen. Both management and the workforce may perceive the need for, or be receptive to, new concepts of work and organisation in the new systems.

12.4 Participation and attitude change
From this we can see the relevance and logic of the participation of those likely to be involved in, or affected by, the introduction of the New Technology, since it is by exposure to the new systems and their implications that existing attitudes and assumptions will be challenged and potentially new solutions determined.

12.5 Organisation design
But what concepts and models of organisation are appropriate to the new technologies and how should they be designed or evolved? Great effort and energy is expended on designing the technical system involved, but how, in what is in effect a socio-technical system, should the corresponding social system be designed and developed.

Group forms of organisation
In the traditional organisation jobs are conceived as independent functions, with any necessary co-ordination being provided by management. In an automated system, jobs tend to be more obviously interdependent since, if one person fails to perform, the overall operation of the process and the product will suffer. Similarly, since the jobs are interdependent, it is important for people to appreciate how their work affects others at different stages of the process. For these reasons it would appear more appropriate to conceive of the workforce as a group, whose members are all involved in the total task rather than simply performing specialised parts of it.

Programming of machines; changing of balance of mental/physical skills
One of the main impacts of computer based automation in manufacture is to remove the manual skill content of the majority of jobs. The mental decisions made by the craftsmen or operators regarding, for example, speed of feed and depth of cut, are now entered into the computer programme enabling the computer rather than the operators to operate the machine.

The traditional approach of specialisation would be to appoint programmers who specialise in this particular task, but this can create communication difficulties between the programmers and those operating the machines. A more effective solution is to give the operators themselves the responsibility of programming and to provide the necessary training to enable them to do this. In this way their skill is retained and the computer becomes an extension and expression of their abilities. Also it can be seen as an advantage that the computer can take over the repetitive physical tasks.

Management of the system

The fact that the computer takes over much of the original manual work clearly means that fewer people need be employed on an equivalent production system. But it also raises the question of the role of management and supervision in such systems. In the traditional structure, the management task is concerned with planning, organisation, co-ordination and control in what was normally a relatively stable environment or assumed to be one. However, in today's circumstances, the system has to respond much more rapidly to changing demands and in this situation a hierarchical management structure, with the communication problems that this causes, is less appropriate. Apart from these reasons the hierarchical structure tends to prohibit the involvement of the workforce themselves in the decisions affecting them and their work. This, apart from having a demotivational effect, means that their potential contribution to problem solving and creativity, in relation to the manufacturing process, is lost.

Thus, from both operational and behavioural points of view, there are strong arguments for the greater involvement of the workforce themselves in the operational management of the new system. As a work group they are close to the process, its problems and its performance. Since they are a work group, recognising the interdependence of their roles there is less requirement for co-ordination than in the old production system. With the aid of the computer and VDU terminals it is possible for the operators themselves to get direct feedback on their work and the performance of the system, together with data on other factors such as stock levels of component, or materials that may be required in the production process. This means that the work group, in possession of the necessary data, is itself in a position to exercise control over its own operation rather than being dependent on supervision.

Flexibility

Similarly, when it comes to the organisation of work, in a traditional system the scope and perspective of an operator was confined to an individual specialised task and thus it was essential for a supervisor to make the decision relating to the allocation of tasks and organisation of work. In the new system, where flexibility is often the key factor, a more delegated approach may be required, where the operators as a group, with knowledge of both the total task and their own skills, can allocate tasks and make decisions about work organisation more readily themselves.

Planning can of course take place on several levels from the overall production programme to the more detailed scheduling of components to achieve the plan. While the decisions of **'what'** has to be made are clearly determined elsewhere by the production and sales managers, **'how'** the plan is to be achieved is another question. At this level, the decisions relating to the scheduling of the work and the changes required in the set up and programmes can be made by the work group themselves.

For these reasons, it would seem that the new computer automated system requires a different management structure from the traditional line. It will tend to be a flatter structure, in which many of the operational decisions will be taken by the work group, leaving management with the 'boundary management' task of matching the outputs of the system overall to the changing needs of the factory and its external environment. Thus, the manager in the new system will be more concerned about overall objectives in terms of output, deliveries, costs and quality than with the detailed direction and control of the labour force.

Relationships with other functions
A similar situation should perhaps apply to the areas of maintenance and quality control. In the traditional structure, the engineering department would take total responsibility for maintenance of the plant and equipment and all maintenance tasks would be performed by specialised, skilled maintenance personnel. The reasoning behind this is that it was assumed that every task required a skilled person to perform it and that removing any concern for maintenance of the equipment would enable the operator to concentrate solely on obtaining output.

In the new system, much of the equipment will be self-diagnostic and therefore while the operators will not be able to rectify electronic faults, their close involvement with the operation and performance of the system will mean that they are very sensitive to possible problems and situations where maintenance services are required. Also, since one minor fault can cause the shut-down of the whole line, as opposed to an individual machine, a close relationship and immediate response situation is called for from maintenance. For these reasons therefore, apart from the added sense of involvement that it affords, a closer relationship and breakdown of traditional boundaries between production and maintenance is required in the new system.

Similarly, with Quality Control in the traditional system, inspection was considered to be a separate function and full time inspectors checked all, or a sample of, the production operatives work. Apart from the overhead costs incurred and the implied assumption about the ability and responsibility of the production workers, defining inspection as a separate function and stage in the production process added considerably to costs and throughput times.

In an automated system, the computer should eliminate human error and thus the need for 100% inspection. If the programme is right in the first place, consistency in quality should be assured unless there are other factors like faulty materials or equipment that cause quality problems. Thus again, rather than employing an extensive inspection staff, the work group itself can assume greater involvement and responsibility for the quality of output from the system, which is both operationally and behaviourally more desirable. In these circumstances, the relationship between Production and Quality Control changes from one of detailed checking, to concern for the quality standards. This can be achieved through the education and involvement of the work force in issues relating to quality and its achievement and in improvements in quality and its costs. Apart from direct involvement in the production system the involvement of members of the team in Quality Circle type activities would also clearly be helpful in achieving these objectives.

The emerging model of organisation that is appropriate to a computer automated system (see Figure 12.3) is therefore very different from a conventional organisation. It breaks with many traditional and strongly held views and assumptions, both by management and the work force and their representatives. The adoption of such forms of organisation, especially in an environment where these traditions have prevailed, is likely to be quite difficult and met with resistance. Further, while the new models of technology may be apparent, those of organisation are less immediately obvious. For these reasons management and the work force may be inclined to stick with the models and assumptions with which they are familiar and feel safe.

Yet while this situation remains, we shall continue to get a mismatch between technology and the use of human abilities which can cause not only dissatisfaction amongst those directly concerned, but also resistance to what in other respects are desirable and necessary changes.

How can we break with traditions and attitudes of the past? How can we help management, technologists and trade unions to appreciate the wider implications of these technological changes? How should these newer models and concepts of organisation be introduced? How can we ensure that a total system approach is adopted? What part should job design take in the development process and how can this best be achieved?

Figure 12.3 New model of production organisation in computer automated manufacturing system

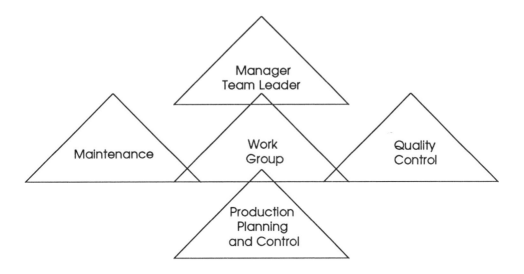

12.6   Role of management

Values, assumptions and attitudes
As has been discussed, much of the problem in the introduction of new technology is not due to the technology itself, but rather the way in which it is introduced. In the robot case study, while the computer has the capacity to release people from the tedious manual tasks to exercise

greater discretion, problem solving and decision making in relation to the process, the way in which it is introduced often has a diametrically opposite result. Thus, relatively skilled, intelligent people are reduced to loading and unloading components onto a conveyor, while senior management and the computer make all the decisions relating to the process.

Managerial prerogatives

This has much to do with the values, assumptions and attitudes about the role of management in organisations held by management themselves, but also, to a large extent, by the workforce and their representatives. As the preamble to the Engineering National agreement says '*Management will manage and the Trade Unions will exercise their functions*'. Thus, management is seen in terms of a right and a prerogative exercised on behalf of the owners by certain designated people whose values, it is felt, still coincide with the owners of the business. However, as the analysis of the robot case study shows, management decisions relating to planning, organisation and control need to be taken at many levels and, as a consequence, need increasingly to be shared within the business. In this respect our situation in the UK contrasts with countries such as Denmark, where national agreements specify collaborative decision making, not only about the strategic development of the firm, but also at an operational level.

Management, as an activity, would be better viewed as a 'Process' rather than a "God given right', to which many people in the organisation can and should contribute if it is to be effective and accepted. This view of the 'process' of planning, decision making, problem solving and control fits much more closely to the 'process' of manufacturing now being employed than the traditional hierarchical model does.

Managerial control

It further relates to managerial motives in the way that new technology is introduced. The mainframe computer accentuates the trend towards centralisation of control since it was necessary for all information to be fed in centrally to the computer, thus providing management with custody of the information and the means of control. The advent of the microcomputer has the potential to reverse this trend since it is now economically possible for decentralised departments and units to collect, process and maintain their own information and control their own activities. However, this possibility may run counter to management's

motives in computerising in the first place. Management may see the more
ready and rapid processing and collection of information as a means of
exercising more effective control of the business and its operating parts.
They may also see a threat to their own positions of authority if the
information on which their ability to control is shared. Thus, fundamental
to the way in which new technology is introduced are the motives (not
necessarily overt or outwardly recognised) of management in the
instigation of the computerisation process.

Managerial role
The fact that information can be collected, processed and maintained at a
local and operational level, as a result of developments in new technology,
does throw into question the whole basis of the traditional concept of the
management role. In a functionally organised company with specialised
tasks, without a computer or having a mainframe, it was essential for
management to collect information in order to co-ordinate and control
activities. Thus, the emphasis in this situation is on a hierarchical
management structure in which the workers do the work and where
management collects information on output performance, stocks, quality
costs etc, in order to plan, co-ordinate and control the operation.   This led,
as some writers have pointed out, to a gap between those that do the
work and those who process the information and make the decisions (see
Figure 12.4).

Figure 12.4 Hierarchical management structure

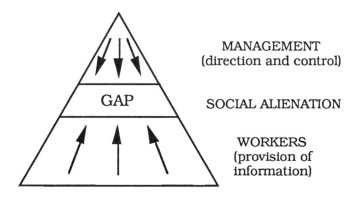

MANAGEMENT
(direction and control)

SOCIAL ALIENATION

WORKERS
(provision of
information)

With the introduction of microcomputers, where a work group can readily
have their own information on all the above factors via a VDU, the work
group itself is in a position to undertake its own operational planning, co-
ordination and control.   This, therefore, raises issues about the

appropriate nature of the management role in these circumstances. As was evident in the robot case study, it would appear that the job of management shifts from one of detailed direction and operational control of staff and activities, to more of a strategic role in terms of development both of the work group as individuals and as a team, but also in terms of the efficiency and effectiveness of the operation and its development. Thus, it is increasingly unlikely that the work group will require direct supervision in the traditional sense and that management will become more concerned with training the skills and attitudes of individuals and communication with, and development of, the group. They will be concerned with issues such as productivity and quality, but more in terms of how this can be improved and developed than by direct intervention and control. Thus, they are likely to work in conjunction with the other departments concerned and with a group in defining and improving standards in these areas. Thus, management's involvement with the work group in a Quality Circle mode might be one of the ways of achieving both the social and economic objectives referred to.

From this analysis it is evident that with such a delegated style of management, greater emphasis would be placed on the 'boundary management' aspects of the role, namely the relationship with other functions and levels within the organisation, representative of the group and their interests, plus communication back to the group on company wide issues and development.

12.7 Strategic and operational management

Group Technology requires Group Organisation as shown in Figure 12.5. To fit an automated situation in which the computer is in effect performing the manual tasks, the work group is, in effect, managing the operation, thus releasing management to concentrate on the necessary strategic and boundary management tasks. In this situation everyone is involved in the 'management process'. Apart from the greater efficiency achieved by computer aided automation, the 'gap' and social alienation familiar with traditional forms of organisation may also be reduced. Whether these results are achieved depends to a large extent on the assumptions and motivations of management in introducing the new technology. If, as is often the case, the motives are cost reduction and the elimination of the unpredictable human factor, then it is unlikely that the strategy outlined above will be employed.

Figure 12.5 Group organisation/technology

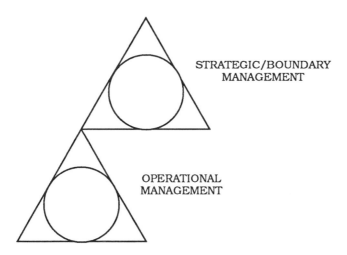

If, however, management values the human contribution as perhaps the most flexible manufacturing or information processing system and sees the computer as a possible extension to decision making and problem solving capacities, then alternative ways of matching people and technology are likely to be employed.   In these circumstances management's assumptions and motivations may well be about increasing overall organisational effectiveness rather than simply reducing costs and, in the long term, this may well be a better route to profitability and survival.

13 THE CULTURE OF THE ORGANISATION

13.1   Organisation culture

The significance of organisational culture has become increasingly apparent as our research has progressed as has its relevance to the issues of organisational change. Early interest was stimulated by Peters & Waterman's book *In Search of Excellence* (1982), which was used by the author as part of a study of management philosophies and personnel policies in the USA (Bailey 1984).

Their work emphasised the importance of identifying and promoting the values which people stand for in running the business, which serves to provide a focus for management, employees and customers alike. Such concepts as closeness to the customer, productivity through people, and management by walking around, were notions with which practising people could identify. While there has been criticism of its universality, their work and its successor in the UK (Clutterbuck and Goldsmith 1984) brought the notion of management philosophy and organisational culture to the attention of practising managers.

More recently, organisational culture has been the subject of more rigorous academic study. The work of Marshall and McLean (1985), while identifying the complexity of the concept, has provided useful frameworks and methods of analysing and identifying the existing culture. Their work and others (Hennestad 1988) has highlighted the double bind which constrains attempts to bring about change in culture. While management may promote concepts such as 'putting the customer first' and 'people orientated management' people's behaviour and long standing practices often send out a different message.

Bate (1988), in his paper on cultural change in British Rail, has stressed the problems of bringing about change in large bureaucratic organisations. However, he argues that an organisation's ability to innovate is a function of its culture, political processes and the competences, personal and interpersonal skills of those involved. In achieving cultural change, he argues, as others have, that it is necessary to help people identify and conceptualise their existing culture. With an understanding of the political processes involved in the organisation, processes which attempt to reform the culture can be set in motion. This clearly calls for different skills than normally found in a bureaucracy in terms of social and interpersonal competencies.

Mumford (1981), in her work at the Manchester Business School, has concentrated on the political processes involved in the introduction of technological change. For example, her research showed the divergence in values and expectations of the clerks and those of the system designers and middle managers. The clerks, for example, tended to want more discretion, while the expectation of the managers and the system designers was for greater control over the process.

In the four cases she studied, integration was achieved either because the system analysts understood the culture and values of the organisation (eg in the Tax Office) or as a result of informal interaction between the systems analysts and the clerks (Chemical). In the other two cases (Asbestos and International Bank) integration was achieved because the system designers were aware of the human needs as a result of the training provided by the Manchester Business School. In these cases the solution was one of self determination where the clerks designed their own form of work organisation. This, it was felt, resulted in three benefits:

i.   It enabled the clerks to determine the form of work organisation that fitted their job satisfaction and efficiency needs.

ii.   It provided them with a learning opportunity and a chance to understand the functions of the department.

iii.   They were committed to the reorganisation and the new system because they played a major role in creating it.

In the latter two cases the system designers, managers and clerks shared important values regarding participation and the organisation of work. In these circumstances the role of the system designer moves to that of a teacher, adviser or consultant rather than being the sole designer.

As a result of her research, Mumford believes that the change process needs to be adaptive and co-operative to cater for changing needs and interests. Planning in these circumstances is therefore creating a structure in which this interaction can take place rather than planning every step. It also demonstrates the importance of values in preconditioning peoples' approach to change. What is needed is a strategy for bringing together the interests of all groups and helping them to identify some shared values about the sort of future they wish to obtain.

Of particular interest from her studies was the fact that two government departments had declined to be included in the book. In these cases the managers' and system analysts' values conformed to theory X, and they did not include job satisfaction as an objective in the new system, or did not adopt a participative approach to the change. In these cases therefore one assumes that the predominant values and lack of interaction had precluded a satisfactory solution and fit between human and technological needs.

The results of her research have been incorporated into a methodology for the introduction of technical change (Mumford 1983) entitled 'The ETHICS Method'. This is based on three essential objectives and value pointers:

i.   The importance of allowing the future views at all levels to play a major part in the design of the system.

ii.   To enable the design groups to set objectives not only in terms of technology and efficiency, but also job satisfaction.

iii.   To ensure that the new technical system is surrounded by a compatible organisational system.

13.2   Culture and technological change

Whilst we recognised the importance of culture at the beginning of our investigation, it did not feature in our analysis of the first few cases. However, as the investigation progressed, its significance has become more apparent and indeed it becomes a focus in the subsequent case studies.

At the beginning of this investigation the concept of culture was based on the ideas of Peters and Waterman and studies of management philosophies and personal practices in the USA. This concept emphasised the importance of beliefs in influencing attitudes and behaviour in organisations towards such values as customer service and quality. This concept of culture has been described as a 'mentalistic' notion by Potter (1981) and others who see culture as the mental programming of a group, tribe or nation towards certain goals, values or beliefs. However, while this approach tends to emphasise the similarities in peoples' view of life, our experience of organisations and more recent research tends to emphasise the differences in peoples' life view. The evidence from Part III in the Paint Spraying Case and the Brewery highlighted significant differences in attitudes, norms and expectations and values.

This suggests that culture has also to do with 'the way things are' and 'the way things are done around here'. Such factors as the structure of the organisation and whether it is formal, hierarchical or bureaucratic, the type of management and the degree to which authority is stressed, the approach to communication and the reliance on verbal as opposed to written communications, all help to create a climate and a prevalent culture which profoundly effects peoples' attitudes and behaviour. Of course such factors reflect the assumptions, beliefs, and values of those people in the organisation in positions of power, namely management whose views may not necessarily coincide with others in the organisation.

This latter view of culture is more consistent with an anthropological approach which emphasises the differences in the values, norms and beliefs of the different participants in the organisation which has considerable significance when it comes to bringing about change.

It is here that the more recent work of people such as Marshall and McLean, Bates and Potter is significant. Their work draws our attention to the contradictions that can occur between the declared values and beliefs of management and those that are perceived by others from their actions. It also draws attention to the significance of the differences between the values and beliefs held by the different groups in the process and to the political and behavioural skills required by consultants and managers in seeking to bring about change. As Potter (1989) suggests, there is a need to recognise what has been described as the etic or emic approach. A succesful change agent needs to adopt the emic approach whereby they recognise the values and beliefs of the people involved with the change rather than seeing things from their own set of values and beliefs, ie the etic approach.

Finally, Mumford in her research on values, technology and work has drawn attention to the importance of identifying the different values held by the participants in the process of technological change and of developing a change strategy that allows these to be shared. The ideal is the development of a concensus about what people are trying to achieve and what sort of life view people can agree upon.

These issues and the significance of organisational culture and its impact on technological changes will be evident in the subsequent case studies.

PART IV

CORPORATE CULTURE
AND TECHNOLOGICAL CHANGE

14 IMPROVING CUSTOMER SERVICE THROUGH EMPLOYEE INVOLVEMENT AND NEW TECHNOLOGY - A CASE STUDY IN THE COMMUNICATIONS INDUSTRY

14.1 Background to company and the case study

With deregulation, which involves opening up competition, the communications industry, like many others such as banking and finance, has become increasingly competitive and the company, like others in the industry, was concerned to improve its competitive position.

Following a report from a major firm of management consultants, which emphasised the need for greater customer orientation, the company launched a programme of decentralisation, creating Districts to provide greater local autonomy, with the aim of improving both business efficiency and customer service. An important part of this programme was an improvement of their customer database through computerisation, and the development of a customer service function that could handle up to 80% of the enquiries received, which they called their front office.

From the outset, the company recognised that this created an opportunity to make changes to the organisation and to peoples' jobs, as well as to the technical system. The change and the use of new technology were seen as major elements in the company's business strategy to improve customer service and ensure its continued development and profitability.

Pilot schemes for their customer service system were launched in several districts and while each district was able to adopt its own approach to the development, a central office was available to provide back-up support, both in terms of the technical developments and also in terms of organisational development and job design.

The investigation focused on the approach adopted by one of the districts which employs some 6000 staff. A number of visits were made to the pilot installation where, with the co-operation of the customer service staff, visits were made to the installation to learn about its introduction and operation.

Responsibilities for the changes being made were shared, firstly by those responsible for systems development, secondly by those concerned with the management of the project in the district concerned and thirdly with the organisation development unit at the head office.

Contact was made with the OD group and the occupational psychologist concerned and this was maintained throughout the introduction of the new system.

Similarly, contact was made with the area manager concerned, who was subsequently appointed as district organisational development manager. This enabled contact to be maintained with the organisation after the change was completed and the project team disbanded.

14.2   Previous situation

In the previous situation, customer enquiries and requests were handled by several separate specialised departments, each of which kept their own customer service records. These were largely on a manual basis, maintained and updated by clerical staff attached to the department concerned. The previous organisational structure, which was acknowledged as being somewhat functional and hierarchical, is shown as Figure 14.1.

Figure 14.1 Previous Organisation

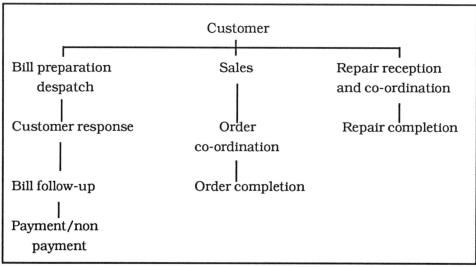

The Personnel Department did a survey amongst the staff and the following comments highlight some of the problems associated with the original structure,

> "*Information not easily available*"
> "*Need to cut down on the paper work*"
> "*Separate working groups do not keep each other informed.*
> "*Parochial views of their own functions, eg sales and billing*"
> "*Records poor and inaccurate. Records about customers will be kept in 15 different areas!*"

These comments were reinforced when visiting the old system which was very antiquated with masses of loose files and tatty paper records kept in very depressing dingy offices.

Within the company, there was recognition of the problems and the need for change.   The existing organisation was cumbersome and inefficient and lacked adequate customer information and orientation. This created problems and frustration for the staff and undermined the service they could provide for the customer.

14.3   The new system

The new system was based on the overall concept of a customer service unit which is seen as the *front office,* able to deal with up to 80% of all customer enquiries and requests.   The object was to get as near as possible to the '*one stop*' shopping concept where staff who are suitably trained and motivated can, with the aid of a computer based information system, process the majority of customer queries and requests.   Today's customer expects responsiveness, commitment, action and feedback and this is what the new organisation and its accompanying technology was designed to achieve.

The new computer system, which was developed by the company's own staff, was based on an IBM mainframe computer of 60 kegabites, providing an integrated database and 1000 terminals throughout the district. It provided *front office staff* with the record of existing customers and all the information they may require in order to process enquiries about sales, billing, maintenance problems and requests.

As frequently occurs with the introduction of new technology, the opportunity was taken to redesign the physical layout totally. A new, purpose-built office was introduced on the site which provided the staff with excellent facilities. These included new purpose-built office furniture, different lighting, and a raised carpeted floor, all of which created a very pleasant light and spacious working environment. Front office staff were provided with a direct computer link with the specialised departments concerned and the revised organisation structure, as shown in Figure 14.2

14.4   System operation

Incoming telephone calls were added to a queue, the first in the queue being taken by the first available operator. At the time of this study the average waiting time for a customer call to be answered was 11 seconds. As an example, one of the operators studied received a request from a customer for a disconnection as the subscriber was moving out of the area. In the space of about two minutes the operator arranged for the disconnection to be carried out, deleted the subscriber from the directory and arranged for the final account to be raised and despatched.

Figure 14.2 New organisational structure

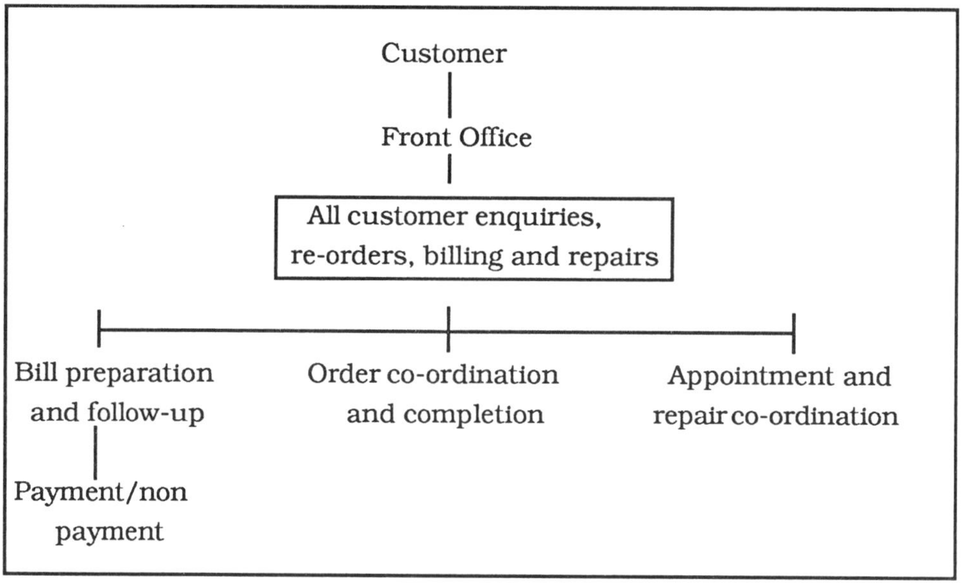

Staff reactions

From the employees' point of view the operators said that they preferred the new job to their former role, eg in billing. It is much busier, more varied dealing with sales, accounts and fault enquiries. The staff in the front office wanted to be near and committed to the customer and it was felt there was a good atmosphere in the office. However, their work was paced to the extent that they have to follow up calls which were waiting and which were indicated by a light on the console. Also, they felt some pressure and responsibility but there was a feeling of not wanting to pass the query on. In practice, staff were dealing with a higher level of enquiries, near 87% rather than the original 80% target, and having to handle up to 50 different types of call. At the time 28 staff were dealing with an average of 2000 calls a day, an average of 71.5 calls per operator per day.

14.5   Introduction of the changes

From the outset, the approach adopted to the introduction of the change by the project management team was that commitment to the new system would only come from involvement. Thus, it was necessary to obtain the commitment of the Board to this development and to answer their questions about the new system. Once the framework had been agreed by the Board and a report outlining the plan had been produced, the project team would delegate the work of introduction to each area.

The Trades Unions, who were concerned about possible job losses and changes to job content, were invited to participate in the planning process and to join in steering groups. Although it took some three months for the unions to decide to participate, an open consultation process was achieved with representatives from six trade unions involved on the steering group which met at monthly intervals. Both management and employee representatives agreed on their lack of knowledge of the new system and therefore drew on a group of specialists and experts to advise them. Both management and grade staff were sent off to learn about the new system.

This joint learning and problem solving approach was further emphasised by the formation of a number of *study groups* involving staff at the lowest level in aspects of the development of the new system. The stated aim of the study groups was to encourage ownership of the new system at the basic level of the organisation, by involvement in the planning process. Typical issues examined by the study groups would be how the new system would affect the billing department and how to manage the introduction of the new system. The structure of the consultative process can be illustrated as in Figure 14.3.

Figure 14.3 Consultation structure

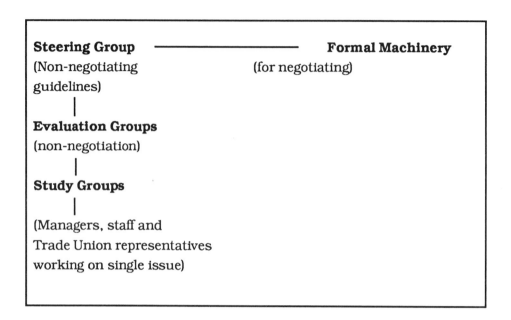

14.6   Selection, job design and training

The development of the technical system was linked with a high level of participation of staff and with a comprehensive training programme for front office personnel. A specialist front office trainer was appointed at the site and with the aid of an occupational psychologist from the head office, staff were invited to participate in a pilot study in the design of their own jobs and in the final detailed aspects of the system development.

From the outset, it was recognised that a high level of training was going to be necessary to change the way people thought about their job. While people were invited to apply for front office jobs on a voluntary basis, most of the staff only had experience of one of the specialist functions, eg billing, sales or repairs. Also, they had been based in the departments concerned and tended to be more orientated to their function than to the customer.

The approach adopted therefore was to lead people into the new situation gently and to let people 'walk before they ran'. They were invited to describe how they would see the new job, what queries should be dealt with and what depth and what training they would require. They were also consulted about the number of calls they thought they would handle, how long a customer should wait, number of staff required and the decisions that they would be prepared to make. Finally, they chose their own office furniture and had some influence on the ergonomic aspect of the design of the new system.

In describing the pilot study, the company's occupational psychologist explained that they set very limited objectives for the first six people involved in what was a process of participative job design. The company's main aim would be for them to familiarise themselves with the new system. Help and advice was offered on a *'take it or leave it'* basis but was not imposed. With the aid of a questionnaire developed by the head office, staff were invited to consider what aspects of their current job they didn't like and what they would do to change it. Thus, the initial objectives were to:

i. Learn the new system
ii. Take over the billing enquiries
iii. Navigate the system and customer records.

After the first fortnight, things were going well but differently to what had been expected. The original manager was not happy with what the new job involved and was not used to a situation in which the staff were able to define their own jobs. The environment had been much more formal and bureaucratic, whereas now the staff were in an open office, stopping and starting work as they saw fit and reviewing their own performance and progress. Initially, there had also been some reaction from the group to working in this way as it was very different from what they had experienced. However, following the appointment of one of the members of the support staff as a group leader they now seemed to be responding very well and identified more with the objective of providing a service to the customer. It was felt that a considerable change in attitude had already occurred in the first two weeks, with a much more positive attitude to the job and a wish to become more involved.

14.7   Conclusions

From the company's point of view, the new system has provided many benefits and opportunities amongst which the following were highlighted by the company:

* The introduction of a front office concept
* Removal of artificial barriers within the organisation

* Dispersal of operational controls
* Centralisation of operational information
* Terminal driven jobs
* Flexible work load management
* Maximising responsibility
* Reducing the grade structure
* Convergence of administration and operational tasks
* Exploiting information
* Territorial/functional review
* Training

Having got the initial system into operation in the pilot area, it is envisaged that further development will involve looking at the end user and the management of problems and enhancements to the systems. Customer service staff are now responsible for training and a team of trainers and a training package have been developed. The company envisage moving to a flatter structure and to a position where the computer system will provide greater integration of all the functions concerned (see Figure 14.4).

Figure 14.4 Integration of functions

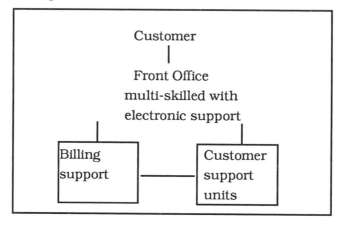

While no systematic data is available on the levels of satisfaction of customers or of staff, it was evident that this development is seen as a very important part of the company's business strategy and future development. It marks a distinct shift from a bureaucratic and technically orientated organisation to a market and customer centred service operation. This has called, not only for more advanced technology and computer based systems of information and integration, but also for changed attitudes, jobs, organisation and communication patterns.

Because of the far reaching nature of the changes, those responsible for planning the project have recognised the need for involvement of all concerned at the earliest feasible stage. This level of consultation and participation does appear to have borne fruit and provided that this change of climate is maintained should facilitate further development.

Finally, it does illustrate that the introduction of new technology need not be at the expense and satisfaction of the staff concerned, but can lead to more varied and satisfying jobs for the people concerned if it is planned this way.

It does, however, demonstrate that change of this scale calls for resources and investment not only in the development of the technology concerned, but also in the human, social and organisational aspects and implications of the change. The experience gained in this case should help in future developments

15 DISCUSSION OF THE CUSTOMER SERVICE CASE

15.1 Focus of the case study

Whereas earlier studies started out at the operations level and progressed to strategic issues, this study, if anything, started at the strategic level and subsequently progressed to issues at the operational level.

The research in this case started when learning about the planned changes in the company at a conference. The manager responsible for the development of their computer system was very sensitive to the human and organisational issues involved. Through his auspices introductions were made to the Project Manager and his colleagues to discuss the development and their approach to its introduction. It was the objective to follow the change at first hand and, if necessary, provide professional job design advice, but the sensitivity of the situation and trade union attitudes prevented external involvement, It was very useful to have the opportunity to work through the OD Unit in London who were involved in the project as a professional resource in OD and job design.

Although there was the opportunity to observe both the old and the new systems and talk to the staff informally, it was not possible to conduct a job diagnostic survey directly. However, the occupational psychologist involved used a questionnaire that had been developed by the company and while it was useful it was not possible to obtain the results of their survey direct, in demonstrating their approach both to job design and the introduction of the changes.

From informal discussions with the staff during visits both before, during and after the change, it was possible to obtain an impression of the jobs and the new system and of the staff reactions to it.

In this case therefore the focus of data collection has been more concerned with the strategic aspects of systems development and organisational change than with the detailed effects on job content. It was more about the strategy adopted to bringing about change in a technically orientated organisation, and it is in this respect that the case study is particularly relevant.

15.2   Management strategy and the need for change

Recognition of the need for change came about largely by a combination of changes in the external environment.

Firstly, changes in the political climate led to deregulation in the telecommunications industry which has opened up the network for private enterprise and competition. This and the Government's policy to end the monopoly of equipment sale has meant that they have moved into an increasingly competitive market. Add to this the very rapid technological changes in the communications industry and it can be seen that the environment in which the company is operating has become much more complex, competitive and subject to rapid change. The intention has been to give the consumer more choice and to give greater expression to market forces.

Colin New (1978), in an article on 'What we need is a Marketing and Manufacturing Strategy', explained the need for the internal organisation to match the external environment in which it is operating. Traditionally the company has had a rather bureaucratic image and structure and has tended to be production rather than consumer led. The changes in the external market now called for a substantial shift to a more market and consumer orientation which would need to be reflected in the structure and style of the business.

It was recognised by those responsible for developing customer services that the current structure with its departmental barriers and manual systems of information would not be sufficiently responsive to give a fast and efficient service. The strategy in the new situation was to give a greater priority to customer service and the speed with which information, advice or action could be taken.

However, while it was recognised that technology in the form of a computerised data and customer services system could help to improve the efficiency of the service a premium was placed by the project team on the involvement of people in the new system and its development. There was the recognition that people, particularly in a service function, are extremely important and that their attitude to the customer and the efficiency with which they could handle their queries are all important to survival in the current climate.

Thus, the concept of the front office as the interface between the customer and the organisation was conceived. This was intended to provide the equivalent of the 'one stop shopping' concept where a properly trained and motivated staff with all the backup that the organisational and technical system can provide could handle up to 80% of a customer's needs.

15.3   Systems development

There are a number of significant factors in the approach to systems development adopted in this case compared to the order office case study.

In this case the primary motivation for the development of the new technical system was to improve customer service. Customer surveys showed that customers would be referred to many different people leading to confusion and lack of a co-ordinated response. The development of the system was therefore clearly linked to overcoming current problems in the strategic objectives and development of the organisation.

Although the system was developed centrally it was designed in such a way that it could be adapted to the needs of the local situation. The problem in the past was in having a large central head office which could be out of touch with local needs. However, in this case staff from the regions were co-opted and seconded to the centre and the end user was involved in the development of the new system.

The technical staff concerned were also aware that the technical system would have organisational and communication implications and that it cut across existing functional and trade union boundaries. Thus, as opposed to the centralised and deterministic approach adopted for example in the order office case, the company demonstrated considerable sensitivity in their approach to the technical systems development. In particular they recognised its implications for strategy, integration and participation.

15.4   Job design

The communication company case is also very interesting in terms of their use of and approach to job design. In the first instance there was a clear recognition of the need for job design in the introduction of the new computer based customer service system.   This recognition may in part have been enhanced by the fact that a new job was being created involving elements of the previous functional tasks (mainly billing, sale and repair). But it is significant that the company particularly recognised the need for job design and were willing and able to devote the necessary resources to the project.   In this respect an occupational psychologist well versed in job design concepts was seconded to the local area for a period of several months to work exclusively with the staff involved with the customer service system on the development of the new jobs and the staff concerned.

However, apart from the fact that they recognised the need and were prepared to allocate appropriate resources, it was also interesting to observe the strategy adopted to job design. In the first instance help and advice in terms of job design was offered   on a take it or leave it basis and was not imposed. The occupational psychologist was available to help the staff with their queries and problems as they arose.   A questionnaire was used to seek opinion of staff about their current jobs to how they felt they would be improved.

Initially a group of the staff were selected from existing functional departments to be trained for the new customer service system front office job. The approach adopted by   the occupational psychologist was initially to work with this group of staff to see what they were doing and to possibly advise on job design when needed and to talk with the manager about the problems.

Having established contact and a 'rapport' with the group they were able to agree limited initial objectives as regards the development of the new jobs. In this first instance, the staff would concentrate on learning the new system. Having done this they would then take on billing enquiries before progressing to system reorganisation and customer records.

Eventually when the staff had gained confidence they would take on the other functions of sales and repairs but as can be seen from the above the approach was very much one of work organisation development and the progressive development of the job and the staff through involvement and consultation.

Their attitude towards the introduction of new technology was that job design is relevant and necessary. It requires resources and expertise which should be offered to those involved rather than imposed. Job and system design should also be on a participative and incremental basis. This contrasts dramatically with the order office case, where none of the above factors applied with predictable results, particularly as far as the staff are concerned.

15.5   Departmental relations

One of the implications of computerised systems of information is the opportunities this can present for the greater integration of related functions. In this case there was an awareness that the introduction of the customer services system could have implications for communication and the relationships between billing, sales and maintenance which were at the time quite separate functions.

The fact that customer services had access to the information on all these aspects could facilitate greater integration and teamwork between these functions for the benefit of the customer.

Although it was not possible to carry out any structured research on the related functions, informally there was some evidence that little change in attitude had occurred in them. In one instance for example, the front office staff had great difficulty in getting someone from accounts to respond to a customer query. From the apparent attitude conveyed, it appeared that accounts staff did not share the same objective as the customer service staff. While opportunities for developments were recognised by the company, it was felt that any structured integrative change to achieve this would represent a further stage in organisational development although it is not clear how and when this might occur.

15.6   Management style

Whilst the needs and opportunities for change in terms of structure appeared to be recognised, it is not certain that the same can be said for management style. There are some indications that there was resistance amongst line management to the delegation of responsibility and greater autonomy for customer service and other staff.

The company has a history of operating with a rather bureaucratic, hierarchical structure in which people are expected to be told what to do. However, the introduction of a system which gives staff greater access to the necessary information for decision making may call for some change in the style of management appropriate to this new situation. In particular, if staff are able to make the necessary operational decisions this should free line management to concentrate more on the development of the people and the system and to operate with a more delegated style of management. How far this has been recognised is not clear. There is some evidence that the prevailing style of management is acting as a constraint on the further development of the customer service concept. In terms of further development of the customer service concept and the quality of service given, it may be that management development, particularly in relation to the role and style of management appropriate to the new situation, could be a priority for the company.

15.7   Management of change

Although in many ways the approach to the introduction of the changes was very effective, there is some evidence from the case that the analysis adopted in terms of planning the change may have been too restricted. While they recognised the human implications, and adopted a participative approach to job and systems design, their approach, in terms of organisational change, was still based at the level of the individual rather than in terms of developing the team. Changes were made to the jobs of the front office staff, without any apparent complementary changes in other related functions, such as accounts and enquiries. However, as the case study shows, improved customer service comes from more effective communication and co-operation between all those who need to work together to give the customer the service they need, and this implies improving teamwork as well as individual job design.

15.8   Conclusions

This case study demonstrates an attempt to use the opportunity provided by new technology to achieve a significant change in culture of the organisation concerned. It is an example of a traditional rather inward looking, bureaucratic and technically orientated company, recognising the need for change in order to survive. Aided by the opportunities provided by new technology, the company was seeking to become more outward looking, customer oriented, people centred and dynamic.

While they would be the first to acknowledge that there is still a long way to go, their initial efforts do appear on the face of it to have been successful. While further research would be needed to measure the effects on customer satisfaction, the effect on employee motivation amongst office staff have been positive. In planning the change they have been sufficiently far sighted to recognise the implications of technical change for job design, and work organisation and for the selection and training of staff; as the project progressed they also became aware of the implications for the structure of the organisation and relationships between departments. However, while significant progress has been made on these factors in terms of change, there is some indication that current management attitudes and style may hinder further developments. This would be a concern for the senior management of such a company because commitment at this level is essential if the changes are to be effective.

15.9 Summary of the questions and issues raised by the communications company case study

This particular case study probably raises more questions about the management of the process of technological change than the detailed changes as such.

In this respect the reader may like to reflect on what the case study suggests about the following broad questions and issues:

i.   What are the relative roles of people and technology in improving the service that the company provides to its customers? How may this affect our approach to the introduction of changes in the technology employed?

ii.   How can we achieve the effective involvement of staff in the design of new systems and what structures of communications, consultation and participation may be appropriate?

iii.   We hear that new technology may imply new approaches to the design and organisation of peoples work. What can we learn from this case study as to how these changes can be brought about?

16 TECHNOLOGICAL CHANGE AND ORGANISATION CULTURE - CONTINUING IMPROVEMENT IN THE ELECTRONICS INDUSTRY

16.1 Background to the case study

Initial interest in the company arose from involvement with the Teaching Company Scheme when it was learnt from engineering colleagues that the company which had opened very recently was very advanced both in terms of its use of technology and also in the style of management being adopted.

Following this, the local Polytechnic was asked to assist in developing an automated system of quality control and a Polytechnic and Company advisory team was established and attention was drawn to the importance of analysing the effect that this might have on staff attitudes towards quality. In a situation where the functions of inspection and statistical quality control were to be automated, an attitude of indifference could arise amongst staff who might consider that the computer had taken over their responsibility for achieving good quality.

The advisory team was very responsive to this view since they had set a very high premium on quality as one of their key strategic objectives. This, plus the fact that they considered that the involvement of their employees was a further essential ingredient to their success, influenced their approach to the project from the start.

Following this, a study was made of their particular approach to management and organisation and a brief paper was presented to the project committee. This paper was well received and provided the opportunity for further involvement with the company.

A project was established to advise the company on their approach to self management and team work and how this could be further developed.

This provided a unique opportunity to examine the nature of the corporate culture in practice and to observe its effects particularly regarding technical change and organisational development.

16.2   The company

The company employs some 100 permanent and temporary staff, engaged in the manufacturing of electronic connectors for use in the computer industry. They operate in a competitive and rapidly changing market, where quality, delivery and customer service are as important as price. Despite the use of automated equipment, they depend on having high calibre technical and operating staff and have to compete amongst other engineering and high tech companies for the personnel they require.

They are in the high technology business and have developed close links with their local Polytechnic and its academic staff. Although the company is a subsidiary of a large multi-national organisation, it is encouraged to operate with a high degree of autonomy.   The firm, which is located in the high technology corridor, is expanding and is engaged in a programme of computerisation and automation of its manufacturing and quality control processes, which it sees as a key factor in its strategic development. However, it is their approach to management and organisation which makes the company of particular interest in that they have sought to develop a distinctive culture and management style. This, they believe, is not only appropriate to their business, but has also given them a strategic advantage over their competitors.   However, they also believe it helps to achieve effective involvement and utilisation of both people and technology.

16.3   Framework for investigation

From earlier investigations it has been possible to identify some of the key factors and variables that influence the effective introduction of new technology. These variables and their relationships provide a framework in which to collect data and analyse this case.

Management Strategy	eg company goals for improved customer service, competitiveness, product design and quality, and the envisaged plans for achieving them, eg introduction of new technology.
Culture	eg the prevailing culture, beliefs and values of the organisation and its influence on the introduction of new technology.

Technology	eg the approach adopted towards system development, the degree of participation in the design process, the extent to which technical and organisational choice and alternatives are recognised and explored.
Organisation Structure	eg the extent to which there is recognition of the impact of computer systems on organisation structure and the integration that can be achieved by information technology.
Management Style	eg the opportunity created by computer aided automation for a more delegated management style.
Job Design and Work Organisation	eg the opportunities to adopt alternative forms of work organisation, eg moving from specialised individual jobs to more flexible forms of group working.
Personnel Policies	eg industrial relations, training, appraisal and reward system, selection, health and safety.

The first stage of the investigation was to establish what the company were trying to achieve in terms of its culture, its strategy, structure and style. What was their intended approach to the use of technology and the related involvement of people?   What was their attitude to the involvement of people and how they approach the introduction of technological change. From discussions with members of the business team and from analysis of published documents and statements, it has been possible to analyse how these factors apply to the company. The results of this investigation form the basis of this chapter. Later in the chapter we examine how far their ideas and concepts are working out in practice based on the evidence obtained from a survey into self management and team work in the company.

16.4   Data collection and the research
The approach to data collection in this case has been of a catalyst collecting and feeding back data on the key issues concerned with the development of the company, its culture and its approach to self management.

Initial investigations into the company, its culture and approach to people and technological change involved interviews with members of the business team and a study of company documents and papers on these topics.

However, as the investigations progressed, it was necessary to have detailed discussions with individuals and members of the self managing teams to establish how the culture and approach to management worked out in practice. This involved interviews with a sample of participants from each of the self managing teams who were representatives of the different grades and functions involved, eg technicians, contractors, office and manufacturing staff. Discussions were held with each group to establish the nature of their work, how far they felt involved, their attitudes towards such things as team work, self management and communication. Use was made of the Hackman and Oldham survey to form the basis of the discussions and to obtain objective feedback on the key motivational job characteristics concerned.

16.5   Business strategy

A key factor influencing the introduction and role of technology is the business strategy of the company. Whether computers and systems of automation are seen essentially in terms of cost cutting and labour savings, as opposed to increasing the flexibility and competitiveness of the company, has a considerable influence on the relative roles of people and technology.

In many sectors of business activity, whether in manufacturing or service industry, the criteria for performance and survival have changed. Whereas in the past the emphasis has been on increased efficiency and cost reduction, today many other factors are required. Organisational effectiveness in today's changing and competitive environment places demands on customer service, quality, choice and flexibility as well as cost reduction, and depending on how they are introduced computerised systems can make an equally effective contribution to these goals and the goal of increased efficiency.

Key goals in the company's strategy are a continuous improvement in customer service and quality and these factors influence their approach to organisation, management and the people. For example, when customers visit the plant it is often the staff who show them around rather than members of the business team, which helps to instil confidence in both the customer and employees. It is stressed that everyone is in a customer/ supplier relationship and this is intended to emphasise the responsibility that all staff have for customer service. Similarly, in terms of quality and the automation of quality control, it is felt very important to retain the commitment of all employees to this goal. The automated systems are designed to enable staff to monitor their own production and quality performance so that they can manage and take corrective action themselves. Quality assurance is seen as an integral rather than separate function in the manufacturing process.

16.6   Corporate culture

Recent research has focussed on the significance of the culture of an enterprise in helping to adapt to change and increase effectiveness. A conscious consideration and declaration of the philosophy, values and principles that the organisation stands for can help both employees, customers, and all those who have a stake in the business identifying with what the business, or board, or management is trying to achieve (Bailey 1984). The work of Peters and Waterman (1982) and of Clutterbuck (1984) demonstrate that those factors such as leadership, management style, attitudes to employee involvement, commitment to quality, continuous improvement and closeness to the customer significantly affect an enterprise's performance and ability to adapt to change.

From the outset, the company has sought to develop a different culture from the traditional approach to management and organisation. Influenced by people such as Deming and their approach of total commitment to and involvement of people in quality, customer service and continuous improvement, the company has developed 'a different way of operating'. Although initiated by the original site manager, the involvement and participation of staff and the technicians achieved considerable commitment to these new concepts. Many of the staff came from traditional engineering backgrounds and environments, and the contrast and opportunity to be treated as a responsible member of the team was like a breath of fresh air and a new experience for many of those involved.

This culture is portrayed in a statement of 'core beliefs' and this is given wide internal and external publicity. Apart from being displayed in every office and conference room, the whole company is very open about its approach and welcomes visits and comments on the way it works in practice. It has been possible to take several groups of students to the firm and no constraints are placed on who one can talk to and what questions people can ask. Similarly, the company values visits from other firms.

All new employees, whether permanent or contract workers, are given a thorough induction to the company and to its different way of operating in particular. Similarly, it commissioned a video to illustrate its approach which helps people to better appreciate what these concepts actually mean in practice.

However, the company is the first to admit that while it may be its intention to operate in a different way, it may not always work in practice. Pressures of time and production may make people slip back into more traditional modes of operation where people are told what to do and are subject to external discipline and control by management. Similarly, technicians may try to act as supervisors directing and controlling staff rather than encouraging staff to take responsibility for their own performance.

For these reasons the company sought external assistance to help review the effectiveness of their approach in practice and how far the ideas of self management and team work were working out in practice. The discussions with the business team and the shopfloor survey have made it possible to form a first-hand impression of their corporate culture in practice and its development.

16.7 Management style

Of particular significance in the introduction of new technology is the style of management. Statements such as not having top heavy management, not policing people and development of an atmosphere of trust, are all intended to imply a certain style of management with a high orientation towards people. The intention is to delegate as much responsibility to the people doing the job as possible, creating local autonomy and accountability through self managing teams. This is reflected in the roles of members of the business team who are described as 'leaders' in that they should provide leadership, support and advice to the teams and the people doing the job, rather than directing and controlling them in a traditional manner.

The concept of a delegated style of management is perhaps best illustrated by their recent introduction of the concept of 'peer group' assessment for all full-time permanent staff. Under this system a member of staff identifies three colleagues, a customer, a supplier and themselves, to review their performance and provide feedback on where improvements could be made. This review is then discussed with the member of staff's nearest leader. This system is intended to reinforce the concept of responsible team work and of self management and improvement. It is also intended to avoid leaders being seen as 'god' in judgement over people but rather in a support and advisory role.

This open style principle of management is also reflected in their approach to the layout of the factory and offices with an open plan system and a single status organisation. The high emphasis placed on communication is illustrated by their use of a 'rack up' meeting every morning with team members to discuss production, safety, quality, people, visitors and any other business.

This style of management clearly also influences other factors and characteristics such as structure, work organisation and personnel policies but, in particular, it influences the approach adopted to change and the introduction of new technology. This is illustrated in their approach to developing an automated system of quality control where a high level of involvement of the staff in the concept of quality and how this can best be achieved has been adopted. In this situation the automated system of quality feedback information is seen as enhancing the ability of staff and team members to take independent action to avoid and overcome problems and to achieve the objectives sought.

Overall, the intended concept is one of self management allowing the people doing the job to run the plant and take the necessary operational decisions, relieving the leaders and the business team to concentrate on the strategic issues and the development of the business.

16.8   Organisational structure

The company has consciously tried to develop a non-traditional organisational structure in the belief that this will lead to a more efficient and profitable operation. Thus, emphasis on hierarchy, formality and independent management control is minimised, the aim being to maximise responsibility, flexibility and autonomous control. The intention is of a low fixed cost and more flexible structure, utilising high spans of managerial control and self managing team concepts (see Figure 16.1).

Figure 16.1 Organisational approach

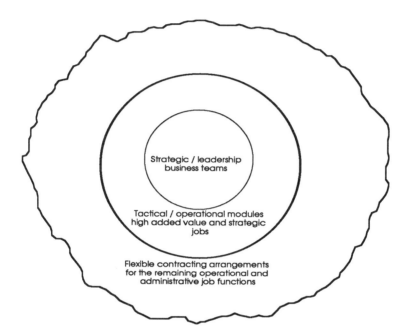

The focal points of the organisation are the core modules of moulding, assembly, warehouse, planning and distribution. Each of these modules is intended to be a semi-autonomous business area and is the responsibility of an identified self management team (see Figure 16.2). The object is for each team to be no bigger than 'eye or ear contact', to understand their internal customer/supplier requirements and have a clear association with their module needs. The teams should 'own' their plant and run the daily operation with absolute flexibility between skill lines.

Management in this situation is seen in a more collegiate/professional role, providing advice, guidance and encouragement and leadership from a strategic point of view.

Thus, their concept is consistent with open socio-technical principles with an emphasis on decentralisation and autonomous business units. It tends towards a flatter rather than hierarchical structure with high degrees of delegation, authority and autonomy at the operating level.

The inherent flexibility of the more organic form of organisation has also been enhanced by the concept of a flexible workforce with core and contract employees. These core employees are employed on the strategic high added-value tasks such as moulding and planning, using contract staff on a flexible basis for the remaining operational and administration tasks. The opportunity is also taken to sub-contract out low added-value non-strategic aspects of manufacture.

16.9   Job design and work organisation

The move towards greater automation in manufacturing brings many functional engineering operations much closer to the nature of the continuous operations associated with chemical and other process industries. This creates changes in the skills required from manual to more discretionary skills but also provides the opportunity for greater involvement of the staff in the management of the operations themselves. Group technology may require group forms of organisation providing a flatter, more flexible and cost effective structure in which the employees themselves take over the responsibilities carried out by the supervisor in the conventional organisation.

This case study illustrates the opportunities afforded, when working with new technology, for choices and alternative approches to job design and work organisation. In what is essentially a socio-technical system, the company has sought to place as much emphasis on the design of the work organisation and on the involvement of the staff as they have on the technology and production processes concerned.

Figure 16.2 Example of process modules

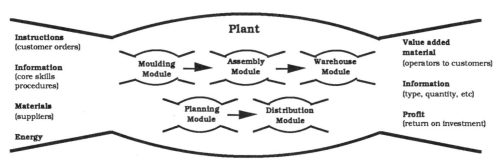

It is the company's stated objective to provide people with interesting jobs and an environment in which people enjoy their work. By 'aiming for a high span of control' and developing the 'self management' concept, the aim is to develop a spirit of team work and to achieve high levels of quality and productivity.

While the goals are set for the teams, it is intended that responsibility for planning and organisation of the work should be delegated fully to the group and shared by team members on a rotation basis. Decisions on shifts, overtime, resources and responsibility are taken by the team members. Team representatives report daily at the 'rack up' meetings on products, performances and problems, personnel safety and quality issues and team members also participate in the selection process for new staff.

The objective of the self management approach to work organisation is to achieve a situation in which staff have a greater knowledge of and responsibility for the products, the process and the customer requirements. They should be able to exercise and develop a greater variety of skills than in a conventional specialised job and structure. The company believes that these factors, combined with the trust that their style of management implies, should help to develop positive attitudes towards the company and to the customers and help to achieve the company's stated core belief, namely:

> "Treat people as if they were what they ought to be and you help
> them become what they are capable of being."

16.10   Systems development

This emphasis and orientation towards people and their importance to business success appears to influence the company's approach to introducing new technology. The development of their systems of automation and information are characterised by high levels of involvement of the staff concerned at all stages of the process. This is illustrated in their approach to the introduction of statistical process control where this is seen as part of the development of total quality management. This places as much emphasis on the attitudes of staff to quality as on an automated system of quality feedback and information. Thus, in working towards more effective quality standards and performance the company has adopted a more integrated approach seeking to develop the technology, the information, the people and the organisation to work towards the new goal.

Initiatives have been taken to set up consultative committees, eg "Continuous Improvement Committees" in which staff are encouraged to suggest what their own concept of quality is and how this can best be achieved. In these circumstances new technology and computer based systems of manufacture and information appears to be less of a threat and more as a strength to peoples' "elbow" in achieving the levels of quality and productivity sought. The company feel that their flexible staffing policy and employment of contractors help to avoid drastic reductions in labour often associated with this type of change.

16.11 Working environment and factory layout

The company's concept of an open and equal corporate culture is reflected in the style of the factory and the physical working environment. One is immediately struck by its comparative cleanliness and the feeling of light and spaciousness. The offices are based on a modular open plan system and it is as easy for someone to walk into and through the plant manager's office as anywhere else. Apart from this, the offices are arranged around the self managing teams and their open design appears to encourage group interaction.

On the shop floor great emphasis is laid on safety and the wearing of safety shoes and glasses. The work areas are clean and bright and are similarly organised around the self managing teams. There are no offices as such on the shop floor and the technicians move readily amongst the operators.

Although there are communal eating areas, there is still a clear physical distinction between the offices and the shop floor due, it is suggested, largely to the problem of noise from the wire cutting machines. This appears to be the only negative factor in a generally pleasant working environment for all concerned. The open plan offices and style of management is intended to make the leaders more visible and accessible and therefore to reduce the hierarchical element and differences in status.

16.12 Personnel policies

It would obviously be inconsistent with their stated beliefs and objectives regarding people to employ divisive personnel policies regarding rewards and other conditions of employment. Reference has already been made to the system of peer assessment recently introduced and also to the selection procedure. However, beyond this, all employees are on the salary role and conditions are harmonised. The company places an exceptionally high level of importance on safety for its staff, for example people have to pass a company driving test before being allowed to drive on company business. Training for staff is provided on a wide basis and many aspects, such as organisational effectiveness and training in interpersonal relationships often reserved for management personnel, are provided for all members of the self management teams.

Finally, no trade unions are officially recognised on the site, the intention being that the level of communication and consultation with staff should ensure that good employee relations are maintained.

Clearly, a number of these policies were quite controversial and in some ways smack of paternalism and wanting to keep the unions out. How effective these policies are and what employee reactions are to them is explored more fully in the following chapter.

17 CONTINUOUS IMPROVEMENT AND CULTURAL CHANGE

Having analysed the company's approach and objective of developing a new culture and a 'different way of operating' it was important to establish employees reactions and how far their intentions worked out in practice. Certain members of the business team felt that while these were desirable objectives there were some problems, particularly in relation to self management and team work. People were, therefore, interested in the idea of a survey amongst the self managing teams to see how far the concepts were working out in practice. There was concern that the motivation and commitment to the ideas did not always materialise in practice.

It was therefore agreed to carry out a survey to look at the issues and provide information for the business team to enable them to continue the development of self management and team work in practice. This was consistent with their concept of continuous improvement and would help to establish how far their intentions had been incorporated into the actual culture of the organisation.

17.1   The survey

In planning the survey emphasis was placed on the importance of taking a socio-technical system perspective. These ideas and the fact that as much effort should be devoted to the analysis and development of the social structure as to that of the task and technology were well received by the members of the business team. Similarly, it was important to incorporate objective measures in relation to the approach to job design and work organisation. How far, for example, in the development of the concepts of self management and teamwork were the goals and desirable characteristics of job design achieved? With the agreement of the businesss team, use was made of the Hackman and Oldham job diagnostic survey to collect data on these issues. Finally, the design of the survey was also influenced by some of the more recent research on the development of high performance and work teams (Buchanan & Boddy 1985) which have been employed in high technology companies. From these ideas and the discussions with the business team, it was agreed that it was necessary to operationalise their approach and establish a set of objectives for the development of effective self management and team work (see Figure 17.1).

At a meeting of the business team about the survey, these objectives were discussed and there was unanimous agreement that this was the ideal situation that they should seek to achieve.

Figure 17.1 Self management and team work

Aim to develop individuals and teams who identify with:

- business goals and their contribution to them
- customers and give them good service
- product, its quality and cost effectiveness
- process from beginning to end
- team and have a meaningful contribution to it
- targets for performance, quality and costs and get feedback on their achievement

---

17.2   Results and feedback from survey

Initial feedback from the survey was given at a workshop with the business team. The company hold regular meetings of the business team to review their operation and this was seen as a useful opportunity to provide some input to their discussions. The report showed that in several respects their ideals were not being fully achieved.

A big issue related to the role and contribution of contract staff who, in many peoples' eyes, were being treated differently to permanent employees and yet, if the company depended heavily on contractors for completing the work, they could ill afford to have anything other than their complete involvement. This problem extended into the area of team work where, in many areas, the contractors did not feel part of the team. The technicians and full-time employees tended to take all the responsibility to the extent of being overloaded and therefore whilst experiencing frustration did achieve a lot of satisfaction, possibly at the expense of other people.

Whilst harmonisation may have existed in relation to terms and conditions of employment, and there were open plan offices, there was still a clear distinction between the shop and office floor. The existence of 'a wall', apparently to deaden the sound of machines, caused a definite feeling of us and them.

But possibly more importantly, these functional divisions appeared to place constraints on the degree of involvement and teamwork that was possible in practice, and the existence of a separate planning and quality function frequently meant that the self managing team was unable to take full responsibility for these aspects of their work.

This situation was further aggravated by apparent uncertainty relating to the roles of the technicians and leaders. The technicians, as their name implies, are better qualified in technical terms than in human and inter-personal skills. Others with large numbers of staff still tend towards a traditional supervisory role than providing effective leadership.

Similar problems occurred with the leaders who, often uncertain as to their role in relation to the self management team, tended to abdicate rather than delegate and to overlook their team leadership responsibilities.

These points were fully discussed at the review meeting and were well received and accepted by the members of the business team.

A further opportunity to provide feedback came at another workshop where it was possible to illustrate the results of the survey using the Hackman and Oldham survey (1980) in particular sections, namely moulding and product assembly (see Figures 17.2 and 17.3).

The contrasting results in these two sections showed the impact that job design, work organisation, technology and the style of leadership can have on the relative degree of involvement and satisfaction of the people concerned. It also helped to emphasise what conditions were required

Figure 17.2 Assembly analysis

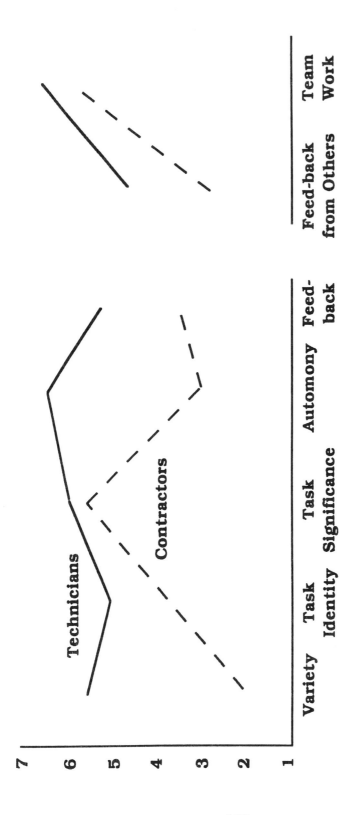

Figure 17.3   Moulding analysis

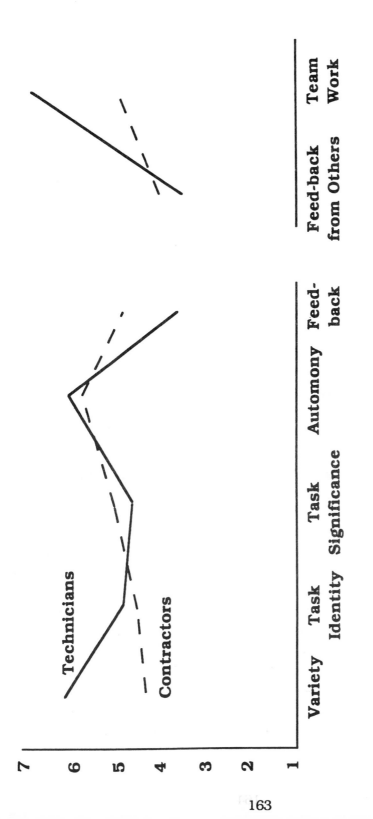

for effective self management and team work which were discussed as part of the presentation on this occasion. A model for effective self management and team work was introduced which emphasised the need for clear and meaningful goals, autonomy and direction in planning and organising the work and for meaningful feedback (see Figure 17.4).

Figure 17.4   Conditions of self management and teamwork

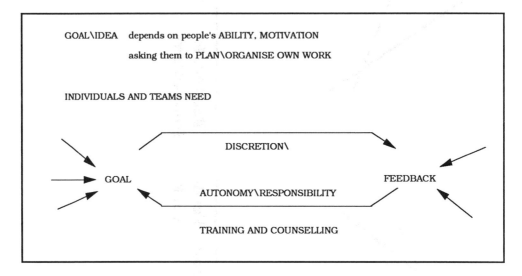

Clearly, however, people are only able to work this way if they have the necessary knowledge, attitudes and skills and this had clear implications for the role of leaders in creating these conditions. Rather than directing and controlling in a conventional way, it was suggested that the role of the leader was more to do with training and counselling the team and their members in how to work this way.

This then led to further discussion about the role of the leaders as members of the business team. It was suggested that evidence from the survey indicated that the leaders were too involved in operational problems at the expense of the strategic development of the firm. This led to discussion of a possible model for the strategic role of the leaders (see Figure 17.5). It was suggested that if they had self managing business teams, who with the necessary technology, information and resources are capable of managing the ongoing operation, then their role was a largely strategic role responsible for the strategic development of the six 'P's, namely people, processes, products, performances, productivity and profit. This clearly gave the business team food for thought, because

Figure 17.5   Strategic role of leaders

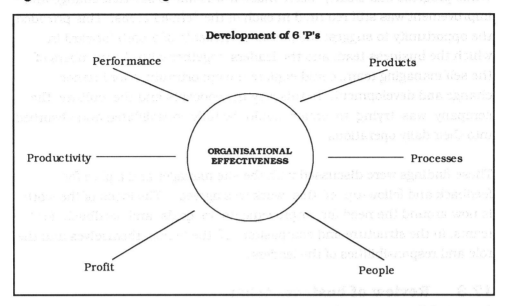

the indications were that insufficient time had been devoted to the development of the leaders, their role and the business team as a team.

Whilst the situation for each self managing team was obviously different, analysis of the overall results indicated a number of common trends. In particular, there was an evident need for clearer goals and more effective feedback for the self managing teams. Too often their goals were defined in output terms only and feedback only occurred if something went wrong. Peoples' experience of variety, and being involved in the whole task, varied considerably from one section to another, but those who were able to see the whole job through experienced much greater satisfaction in terms of variety and task identity.

The latter does have implications for another issue which emerged in terms of team work and team composition. There were suggestions and indications that creating more multi-disciplinary teams responsible for all aspects, including functions such as planning and quality control, might be more effective both in terms of peoples' motivation and commitment, but also in terms of the objectives the company is trying to achieve, namely improved competitiveness, quality standards and customer service.

The report concluded with an assessment of the extent to which the goals agreed for self management and team work had in fact been achieved.

While progress had clearly been made it was fair to say that change and improvement was still required in each of the defined areas. This provided the opportunity to suggest the possible elements of a path forward in which the business team and the leaders, together with the members of the self managing team, could explore the opportunitites for further change and development. In this way the concepts and the culture the company was trying to create could be fully consolidated and absorbed into their daily operations.

These findings were discussed with the site manager and a plan for feedback and follow-up of this work was agreed. The focus of the work is now around the need for improvements in goals and feedback for the teams, in the structure and compositon of the teams themselves and the role and responsibilities of the leaders.

17.3   Review of business team

As part of the review and process of continuous improvement, it was suggested that a survey should be conducted into the role and structure of the business team and of its individual leaders. From earlier studies it had become evident that there was a need to help the individual leaders clarify their own roles and responsibilities, particularly relating to their development of self management and team work.

As a further extension of the work with the company, this survey was carried out within the eight members of the business team and a number of other key people who, it was felt, would have a useful contribution to make on this issue. The object of the survey was to help the individual leaders review their contribution in the light of the changing environment in which the company was operating and to develop effective self management and team work amongst the business team.

The results of the survey indicated that there was a need for the company to review both its strategy and its structure in the light of changing business conditions. This would involve the creation of a number of smaller more autonomous business units in which the leaders would take full responsibility for their operation and development. This implied a major change in the role of the business team and its members which would become more concerned with the strategic development of the firm rather than the day-to-day operational issues. It also implied a change in the role of the individual leaders who would now

166

be responsible for all aspects of the operation of their 'business' and for the team and its development.

In summary, the report, which was well received, indicated a need for an integrated programme of strategic, organisational and leadership development. The first phase of implementation took place with the appointment of the leaders to their teams.

17.4   Management of change

Apart from its interest in terms of the company's culture and their approach to management and organisation, the significance of this case study is the company's approach to the management of change.

Although they are in the high technology business there appears to be a real concern for people and appreciation of the 'socio-technical' nature of the business. While there is an emphasis on business and technical development, the need for complementary developments in terms of the people and the organisation have been recognised. This socio-technical perspective, together with the concept of continuous improvement, has helped to ensure a positive approach to technological and organisational change.

Analysis of the company and their approach to developing the culture of the firm showed that change and development may be required in each of the following aspects. Change and improvement have been sought and achieved not only in terms of their business strategy and the technology employed, but also in terms of the role and style of management, the structure and organisation of work, the people, their knowledge, skills and attitudes and their personal and employment policies.

Their approach to achieving these changes has been through the involvement and participation of those concerned. There appears to be recognition that essentially we are looking at a process of technical change and organisational development.

The company has invested quite heavily in what they describe as 'organisational effectiveness' techniques which influence their approach to tackling problems and managing change. These techniques which are grounded in theory try to ensure that sufficient thought and planning is put into any problem-solving activity and process of change. Members of the business and self managing teams are trained in these techniques and all meetings have to be monitored from a process point of view. At all meetings of the business team, for example, an 'organisational effectiveness resource' is made available to monitor the process and give comment and feedback during the meetings. This emphasis on 'the process' aspects of problem solving is further evidence of a more enlightened approach to managing change.

While clearly there is still room for further improvement, the culture of the company and their approach to management and organisation have helped to ensure the more effective integration of both human and technological needs.

17.5   Questions and issues arising from the case study

This case study raises a number of interesting issues and questions about the problems and processes of technical and organisational change. The following questions may help the reader to reflect on these points:

1.   What is your understanding of the concept of organisational culture and what is its relevance to technological change?

2.   How would you describe the culture in this company and what was its strategic significance?

3.   It has been said that new technology requires new forms of management and organisation. What form did their approach to management and organisation take and how far did this help to integrate human and technological needs?

4.   What does self management and teamwork mean in practice within this company and what are its advantages and limitations?

5.   What is your understanding of the processes of 'continuous improvement' and what does the case study show about its operation in practice?

6.   What lessons can we draw from the case study about the whole question of technological change?

PART V

RESULTS AND CONCLUSIONS

**IS IT POSSIBLE TO INTRODUCE NEW
TECHNOLOGY IN A HUMAN WAY?**

18 WHAT CAN WE LEARN FROM OUR INVESTIGATIONS?

Introduction

The object of our investigation has been to find out whether it is possible to introduce new technology in a human way. At a time when computers and automation are increasingly dominating people's working lives, the question is whether this has to be at the expense of people and their sense of involvement and satisfaction with their work.

While this question is important in human and sociological terms, it is also relevant to the efficiency and effectiveness of organisations. With increasing emphasis on factors such as quality, flexibility and customer service, the attitudes of staff to the organisation of their work and the customer is all important. People will not experience a sense of responsibility and commitment if the results of computerisation have effectively taken their job interest and responsibility away. As Davis (1979) suggested there is a fundamental contradiction where organisations can spend large amounts of money on training programmes to try to make people feel involved and responsible (eg in customer care training and quality circles), but still treat them as automatons on the job with meaningless repetitive tasks with no real responsibility or involvement.

18.1 Effects of technology on people, their jobs and satisfaction

From previous research and the experience of industry it has been possible to demonstrate the contribution that job design and new approaches to work organisation can make to improving both efficiency and job satisfaction. With the ever increasing rate and scope of computer-isation of manufacture and information systems, the question is 'what effect was this having on people, their jobs and their sense of satisfaction and involvement'. Does computerisation add or detract from the desirable

171

characteristics of people's jobs such as meaningful goal, responsibility for decision making, variety, feedback and opportunity for social interaction. Is the popular image of the computer as the enemy of people reducing them to a race of screen watchers and machine minders a realistic picture? What contribution could job design make in this new situation? These are questions that we need to know the answers to and which are very important to society in what is an increasingly technological age.

Our investigations therefore began very much at the level of the individual and the impact of technology, on the nature and content of people's work. From this initial study we found that while the results varied from one application to another, whether technology had positive or negative effects on people and their jobs was not so much a factor of the technology itself, as the way it was introduced or applied. Thus, while the impact on factors such as task identity, variety, autonomy, social interaction may often be negative, this is more as a result of the assumptions made about the relative roles of people and technology rather than of the technology itself.

This, therefore, leads us to the next question, as to *whether or not it had to be this way?* Is it not possible to introduce these systems in a human way? Our hope and belief was that it was possible and that where the right attitudes prevailed and where the knowledge of job design was utilised effectively, it should be possible to design new systems that meet both the needs of the people and the technology. Our faith in this as a possibility has been profoundly influenced by the continued and renewed relevance of socio-technical systems theory. This approach and the perspectives involved, while developed in the early 50's, seem to have a new relevance to the current situation and the application of new technology. The model of the interdependence of social and technical systems does have an inescapable logic which is also well received and appreciated by people in the field (Trist 1981).

18.2   Does it have to be this way?

Having identified an article about what was described as the *'factory of the future'* in which a small group of people as a team were running an advanced factory employing computers and a high level of automation it seemed important to follow this up. As it proved in practice the flexible manufacturing system not only employed the latest in terms of computerised manufacturing and management information systems, but also achieved a high level of involvement for the workforce as a result of employing group working and flexibility. While this may have been chosen for largely operational reasons, it illustrated very effectively that alternative forms of work organisation could do much to overcome some of the negative consequences of the arbitrary introduction of new technology. It was, in effect, an example of the application of group forms of organisation alongside group forms of technology and apart from being 'humane' it also proved to be remarkably efficient and effective in terms of costs and effective in terms of delivery and lead times (Mark 1981).

However, it was not insignificant that this factory was developed as a new small unit on an industrial estate in a small market town some miles from the main factory. It was for the company in many senses a pilot scheme and feasibility study and despite consultations and the positive attitudes of the unions towards these developments, the experiment was relatively insulated from the company as a whole. The question that therefore arose out of this particular case is whether in 'normal' circumstances it is possible to arrive at a similarly acceptable solution and how to achieve this. While the FMS example was illustrative of what was possible in terms of technical and organisational design, the circumstances of its evolution were, to say the least, very favourable. In a more conventional setting, with the traditions of managerial control, hierarchy, demarcation, restrictive practices and resistance to change, is it possible for such radical and imaginative solutions to be created?

The answer to this question also came about as much by accident as design. Involvement with the next company on organisation and job design led to awareness of their project on the automation of aircraft loom building. This they had approached initially in what they described as a classical engineering way utilising job analysis and work study techniques, combined with production engineering and computer systems technology. However, when they came to display a model of the new system, someone suddenly noticed that they hadn't included the people in the model and, what was more, they hadn't really decided what the people would be doing in the new system anyway. This was something of a watershed in their own thinking and their approach to the development and introduction of new technology. Because, from that point on, they decided that they needed the involvement of the loom builders themselves, not only to achieve their acceptance of the new system, but because they needed the experience and expertise in loom building to develop effective alternatives to the traditional manufacturing methods.

The fact that the group described what they were doing as 'job design' was also fortuitous, but they were quick to learn about the value of participative job design to the successful development and introduction of new technology. This case study, while it provided an invaluable illustration of participative job design, also provided some fascinating evidence of the role of technologists in technical and organisational change. The project manager responsible for these developments in the research and technology division experienced something of a transformation in his own ideas and approach to technical change. The experience and success of the loom building project profoundly affected the company's subsequent approach to the development of new technology and its application to the business. The research and technology division came to recognise they were initiating both technical and organisational change and development and that as technologists they needed to appreciate the social effects of the changes they were promoting. It was therefore necessary for the division to possess or have access to the necessary social skills and resources and to build job design and organisation development concepts into their strategy (Mills 1984).

Thus, in relation to the question of *if and how it is possible to create acceptable solutions from both a social and technical point of view*, the loom building case does provide an illustration of what was possible. The fact that it happened as much by accident as design does not detract from the fact that it was possible. Furthermore, there is evidence from the case that it is possible for people and the participants in the change process to learn from the experiment.

In this respect, the role of the project manager as a change agent is extremely important. Having a background that was essentially technical, he acquired from his own studies and experience a wider perspective on these issues. He was in a sufficiently important and pivotal position in the organisation to have some influence over events. His role and influence in bringing about technological and organisational change was very important and helped to achieve some changes in the strategy employed and in the culture of the firm. He had both a 'mission' and the power to act.

The other important thing that comes out of both of these two illustrative cases is the potential and opportunity that new technology provides for change. Because of the power and scope of the computer and the far reaching changes implicit in systems of manufacture and information processing, these changes can have important destabilising effects within the organisation concerned. This can provide a unique opportunity for unfreezing existing attitudes so that prevailing practices, procedures, relationships and ways of working can be 're-examined' in the light of potential change. Capitalising on these opportunities by effective involvement of the people concerned can make all the difference to a successful process and acceptable outcome in which change has occurred on both social and technical fronts. However, as the project manager and his colleagues came to realise, these aspects need as much in terms of knowledge, skills and expertise as do the developments of the technical side. The question is why do so few companies seem to realise this?

The loom building case provides indications of the importance of the prevailing organisational climate in influencing the approach to technological change. The influence of the research and technology division and emphasis on the need to take human and social factors into account probably carried greater weight in a technologically based company because they were technologists. The role played by personnel specialists in this important field often appears to be minimal, if not non-existent, and it seems that it is only when other technologists adopt this position, whose views are respected, that it is possible to influence attitudes on a wider basis.

18.3   Why is job design so rarely used?

If the first two cases in our investigation illustrated what **is** possible and desirable, the second two cases illustrated the possible but undesirable consequences of technical change.

When so much is known about job design, why is this knowledge not used? In what is often described as the second industrial revolution, why have we not learned the lessons from the first? When there is evidence that it is possible to match human and technological needs, why does it so rarely occur?

Insights and evidence on these issues arose from the two cases in the third stage of our investigation. In both cases the approach to the introduction of technology was dominated by technical and economic considerations and, as a result, human and social factors were largely ignored. The results in both cases were, that while savings were achieved, this was at the expense of human involvement and satisfaction and probably of the longer term interests of the companies and their customers.

The first of the two cases, the introduction of an automated paint spraying system employing a robot, was, in many senses, the turning point of the investigation. At this point there was a unique opportunity to be involved and have some influence on the outcome in the introduction of the new system.

However, having expressed interest at being involved and having been invited to attend the planning meetings, it was apparent that the die was largely cast. The system and its feasibility had already been determined with little or no effective involvement of the people concerned or study of its impact on their jobs or satisfaction. While it was acknowledged that the resultant jobs could be boring, it was felt that this was an inevitable price to be paid and that the jobs weren't very satisfying anyway. It was felt by management that the staff would be grateful for having cleaner jobs and were not really bothered about being involved.

Despite the fact that a study on the paint sprayers was conducted which showed that they derived considerable satisfaction from their work, the threats that the new system posed were largely ignored with the pressures to introduce the new system and get the shop operational again. It was only after the event that these predictions became apparent to all concerned when morale and performance in the paint shop hit an all time low (Bailey 1986).

As a result of these experiences, some improvements were made in the technical system and in the working conditions. However, although a new supervisor was appointed, who attempted to involve the staff more as a team, these efforts soon floundered in the prevailing technical and production orientated climate. The solution proposed by management rather than to propose any ideas of greater involvement was to downgrade the job on the paint line and to transfer the skilled paint sprayers to other jobs in the factory.

Thus, we come back to the original question of why doesn't it happen? Why, in a situation such as this, where the knowledge of job design existed and where the expertise was readily available, were the human and social factors overlooked?

Analysis and observations on this case suggest that this was due to a number of factors all of which influenced the climate of the organisation in which the new system was introduced. These factors which included their strategy for introducing the change, the management structure, the style of management, their assumptions about people and their motivation, the industrial relations climate and their approach to systems development, all contributed to a culture in which people are seen as subservient to the machine and to management requirements. The culture is one in which 'management still manage' and employees will do as they are told. In these circumstances, technology is seen as a means of minimising human involvement in the process, thereby reducing costs and increasing management's ability to control.

Job design however is about giving people space and the opportunity to take responsibility and be involved. Such an approach however is quite alien to the environment and culture provided in this and many other industrial companies. Management appeared to be operating with a quite different model and concept of people, viewing them more as machines than people, and applying engineering models not only to the technology but also to the form of management and work organisation adopted.

The suggestion is that new technology requires new forms of management and organisation. While, theoretically, a group form of organisation in which a team of people without direct supervision could have run the paint shop the chances of such a solution being accepted or surviving were minimal. It would have taken a major change in attitude and in the culture of the organisation for such radical measures to have even been considered.

These findings were very largely reinforced by the second case study of the computerisation of an order entry system. In this case the company had been operating with small multidisciplinary teams and a high level of employee involvement in their distribution department. Indeed, the company and their Distribution Manager had won the national distribution management award for the innovation which they had achieved. However, despite this experience and the potential learning that this could have afforded, changes in personalities and in the climate, both external and internal, dramatically influenced their approach when it came to introducing technological change. In the interests of cost reduction, the more effective utilisation of resources and of management control, the new computer system was designed and introduced with a minimum level of involvement of the people concerned. The teams were disbanded and the functional divisions re-established. Motivations for staff were based on bonus incentives schemes with the focus on products and sales rather than customers and service. This system, when combined with the changes to the trunking and delivery arrangements, meant that more of their faith was placed on technology and the people had to fit around these new systems whether they liked it or not. Again, how far this was in the best long term interest of the company is a somewhat open question. While short term gains in cost reduction, increased sales and greater efficiency may have been achieved, this was at the expense of the involvement and satisfaction of the staff. How far this could also affect people's attitudes to such issues as quality and customer service is also, to some extent, debatable, although in today's environment these aspects are increasingly important. It comes down to how far technology is seen as part of the company's longer term strategic development or as a short cut to cost reduction and greater efficiency.

However, one of the most important conclusions to be drawn from this stage of the investigation is that *even when the knowledge exists, when the opportunities are provided and when the expertise is available, there is still no guarantee that the social factors will be adequately considered.* Whether they are or not is a function of the attitudes and assumptions of those people involved and of the prevailing climate and culture of the organisation concerned.

Thus assumptions and attitudes towards such factors as:

❑   corporate strategy and technology
❑   company philosophy and culture
❑   systems development
❑   management organisation
❑   job design and work organisation
❑   personnel development strategy
❑   industrial relations/employment policies

can vitally affect the way the technology is introduced and whether a satisfactory socio-technical result is achieved.

The question that now arises is *if these conditions are important how can they be achieved?* What possibilities exist for influencing the climate and culture of the organisation and how can changes in these factors be brought about? It is not without significance that in both the preceding cases there was no internal 'change agent' with a socio-technical perspective. Those involved in designing the new system were either production technologists or systems analysts and did not appear to have any appreciation of the social implications of the changes they were initiating. This lack of awareness, and the fact that the personnel functions were not involved either because they were not invited or failed to take the initiative to be involved, meant that there was nobody acting in the role of 'guardian angel' for the people and social factors involved. The passive trade union situation in the two cases meant that there was little pressure from that quarter either, which effectively gave management and the technologists their head. Key individuals with both power and a socio-technical perspective may therefore be an important factor in creating the necessary conditions for socio-technical change.

18.4   Creating the conditions for effective socio-technical change

The issue of the final stage of our investigation is therefore *how far it is possible to create the necessary conditions for effective socio-technical change.* What are the elements and organisational conditions that are required and how can they be created? Insights and evidence on these issues came from the two complementary case studies in the final stage of our investigations. The first case of a telecommunications company involved the introduction of technological change in a traditional, technically orientated and bureaucratic organisation which involved all the problems associated with change in this type of environment. This contrasted however with the second case which was a green field site where, by contrast, there were virtually no constraints on what was possible in terms of socio-technical design. The interesting feature of the telecommunications case was the fact that, despite it being a very technically orientated company, those responsible for processing this change were very sensitive to the social and organisational implications of the new systems. The case contrasts with the preceding two cases, and corresponds with the loom building situation, in that here there were 'guardian angels' who recognised the technical changes as an organisational development programme and a process of cultural change.

Their perspectives clearly had considerable influence on people within the organisation and on the whole approach to change. For example, at the level of job and system design, although the overall concept of the customer service system was developed by the company technologists, staff were involved in the detailed aspects of design, particularly at the level of the machine/human interface. The need for job design expertise was recognised and utilised, but this was not imposed on people but made available as required. As a result, the case illustrates the value of what was a very effective process of participative job design and organisational development. Thus, in socio-technical terms, thought had been put into developing both the socio-technical systems which resulted in a very satisfactory match from both a performance and job satisfaction point of view.

Equally, however, the overall project manager, with his OD role and perspective, had considerable influence within the organisation and with the interested parties concerned. He worked with the Divisional Board of Directors to get their comments on the new system and set up an elaborate committee structure with the trade unions and employees. Their use of 'study groups' to involve people at the grass roots level in the implications and particular aspects of the new system seemed to be particularly valuable and these groups fed the more formal evaluation and steering groups.

Despite these efforts problems still existed in the commitment of middle management and the related service function of accounts and maintenance to the new system and the approach required. The appointment of an OD Manager for the division, is evidence of the continuing concern for these issues.

However, changes in personnel meant a change in emphasis with greater pressure for performance and output. This, to some extent, created a change in the climate and organisation and represented something of a setback in achieving the cultural change envisaged.

Thus, in relation to the original question of how far it is possible to create the necessary conditions for change, the telecommunications case is very illuminating. It suggests that if there are people, particularly technologists, with a socio-technical perspective and if people recognise that it is a process of organisational development as well as of technical change, then it is possible to create the conditions for such changes to occur. Whether this can be sustained however is another problem as this case clearly demonstrates as the climate of an organisation is very difficult to change.

The final case study helps to throw some further light on this particular issue of how to sustain the process of socio-technical change. Interestingly enough, this company was identified by an engineering colleague. He was aware of the social aspects of technological change and as a manufacturing systems engineer was sensitive to these issues himself. He thought that the company would be interesting because not only were they a high technology company, using new technology and computer based systems of manufacturing and information, but they also had developed a very different and distinctive approach to management and organisation. It would therefore be very interesting to learn more about their approach and to assess how far what appeared to be a socio-technical approach worked out in practice.

The significant thing about the company was their fundamental commitment and belief in people as their key resource. This philosophy is based on the tenet that 'if you treat people as if they were what they ought to be, then they will become what they are capable of being'. The phrase, while possibly sounding a bit patronising, nevertheless profoundly influenced their whole approach to management, organisation, technology and people. The form of organisation with its emphasis on self management and teamwork, the style of management with its emphasis on leadership and support, the flat collegiate structure with its lack of emphasis on hierarchy and authority were all designed to give people a real sense of involvement and responsibility. This, coupled with the emphasis on communication, open planning and single status, was designed to help people feel that they all have an equal part to play in running the business and satisfying the needs. While a survey conducted at the plant found many areas that needed improvement, their approach, the involvement and commitment achieved, in comparison to the average industrial organisation, leaves other companies standing. This was borne out by talking to the technicians themselves, many of whom came from traditional engineering companies and none of whom would go back to the sort of situation that they experienced there. By way of illustration a toolmaker from a more traditional firm was asked what percentage of his possible contribution that company permitted him to give. As suspected he said that it was no more than 50%, but that was not because of his attitude but because of the system, the approach and attitude of management in the company concerned. Companies like the one in the case study realise that apart from the waste in human terms they cannot afford this situation in the highly competitive market in which they are operating. They have to be slim, highly flexible and very efficient in order to stay in business and this means achieving the total involvement and commitment of their work force.

A further significant feature of the electronics company is their openness and their commitment to the concept of continuous improvement. Unlike the telecommunications company, who were very sensitive to external involvement and influences, the electronics company are openly exposing themselves and their way of operating to outsiders and visitors, but also drawing heavily on external sources of advice and support. This, coupled with the commitment to the continuous improvement of all aspects of their business, helps create an orientation to change. Thus, in terms of technology, tasks, process methods, and procedures, staff are expected as part of their role with the company to be continually looking for better ways of doing the job. The company did not see the need for quality circles or suggestion schemes which they see as devices in traditional companies to enable employees to propose changes for management to consider. They feel it is part of the employees' responsibility to seek better ways and implement them and to inform their leader what they have been able to achieve.

However, this total involvement and commitment to continuous change and improvement can only come if the right supportive climate exists. This was shown in the earlier research on work restructuring where an umbrella and safety valve have to be created in which employees can feel secure to participate and initiate change. Nobody is likely to willingly identify, initiate and implement change unless they feel their own interests and security are safeguarded. It is in this respect that the climate and culture that was developed in the electronics company was so important. This culture, with its commitment to the staff and their involvement and development, to the customer and the quality of product and service given, to the concept of continuous improvement and a management that will not stand over or police people, helps to achieve the degree of responsibility and security required. The emphasis on the culture of the organisation and the way they want to run their business helps to create a 'stability' within which change and improvement can occur. In these circumstances changes in technology are not seen in any way different to other changes in the organisation and the involvement of people in the process is taken for granted. The technicians, apart from their leadership role with the self management teams, are continually looking at ways of improving the processes and are implementing changes within their own operations. Good job design has followed naturally from this stated philosophy and from their belief in people.

Through the self management teams people have been given the space to make decisions, solve problems, work together, learn and develop, innovate and make change. If anything, the problem is not one of involvement and satisfaction, but one of overload. The leaders and technicians in particular complain that they have too few resources to do the job. The other problem is how to maintain personal development and progression in what is essentially a very flat structure and the technicians often complain that there is no future or promotion prospects for them. Part of the problem, as the survey indicated, comes from the use of contractors, where people see the contractors as a pair of hands and are not prepared to delegate responsibility to them. This means that the contractors themselves are often disillusioned and see the jobs purely in instrumental terms.

So while there are problems, and no one saw what they were doing as perfect (indeed that would be a contradiction in terms), this case study does provide some invaluable clues as to how the process of 'effective socio-technical change' can be sustained. Not only does it mean an awareness of the opportunities for technological innovation or of the needs and opportunities for change in the social structure, it also means a commitment by management to creating the type of climate and culture where people can with confidence participate in improving the effectiveness of the business and take the initiative in doing so. In this context management becomes much more of a 'process' in which everybody can participate rather than the prerogative of the privileged few.

19 CONCLUSIONS ON THE EFFECTIVE INTRODUCTION OF NEW TECHNOLOGY

Reflecting on the research and what this investigation has been about one is conscious of the fact that in trying to bring about socio-technical change we are dealing with two fundamentally different entities. Technology, by its nature, is 'concrete hard and set' and therefore you need to uproot it sometimes with a pneumatic drill to replace it. People by contrast are living, and are therefore capable of growth, adaptation and development. The two sides of the coin are in many senses completely opposed and different.

19.1   Effects of technology on people

However, technology can constrain our ability to manage our own work and activities. This was evident from the earliest days of management in F W Taylor's (1947) work in the Bethlehem Steel Company. Here, his study of men shovelling coal caused him to define and constrain their approach by determining such factors as the size of shovel, the speed of work and the manner by which the shovel (technology) should be used. These constraints and the institution of functional management with the gang and speed bosses effectively destroyed man's scope of responsibility and motivation which had to be replaced by external financial incentives.

The earlier work on alienation (Blauner 1964) and on peoples' reaction to assembly line work (Walker & Guest 1952), also demonstrates the negative consequence of technology on people and their sense of involvement and responsibility. Similar results were also obtained when Blauner's ideas on alienation were tested out on banking and insurance workers (Kirsck and Lengermann 1972). These showed that feelings of meaninglessness and estrangement increased with the degree of automation or mechanisation involved. Their study identified three factors most strongly connected with feelings of estrangement and alienation, namely lack of control over the immediate work process, performance of narrow work roles due to advanced specialisation and lack of opportunities for promotion.

Thus, the original question which led us to this investigation is, in what is often described as the second industrial revolution, have we learned the lessons from the past? Does the introduction of 'new technology', ie computer based systems of manufacture and information, also have to be at the expense of people and their sense of involvement and satisfaction? What are the consequences of the introduction of computer based systems on the nature of people's jobs and, if it is negative, does it necessarily have to be this way? If not, what is the alternative?

As individuals with an interest in people and job satisfaction and having some knowledge of job design, what contribution can these ideas make in this situation. Can job design contribute to the effective introduction of new technology, and if so, in what circumstances does this apply?

If this was the starting point for the research, what have our investigations shown and where have we finished up?

19.2   Progress of the investigation

While the research started at the level of the individual and their jobs, our investigations and the factors raised have led us to examine wider issues at a higher level within the enterprises concerned and in the environment in which they operate. Thus, our perspectives, data collection and analysis have progressed from the individual and the nature of their jobs, through the level of work organisation to such issues as strategy, structure, communications and interdepartmental relationships. It has, however, also involved issues such as the role and nature of management in enterprises employing advanced technology and the implications that this has for the overall climate and culture of the companies concerned.

In addition to these features which relate largely to the design of jobs, work organisation and corporate structures, the other feature of the research has been the increasing emphasis on the change processes and strategies required. Thus, as the research has progressed, we have found the need to concentrate increasingly on the factors that enhance or inhibit the changes required and what this implies in terms of style of management and cultural change. (See Figure 19.1)

This has meant that, as the research has progressed, the relevance of the thinking on open systems and socio-technical systems theory has become increasingly relevant. The research has also shown the relevance of the literature on strategy and organisational development to the introduction of technological change and its links with corporate culture. We started with a belief in the value of job design to the introduction of new technology. We have ended up with recognition of the relevance of corporate strategy and culture to the successful implementation of change. In fact, both notions are important to the effective introduction of new technology and to the resulting match of human and organisational needs.

Figure 19.1 Progress in levels in the research investigation

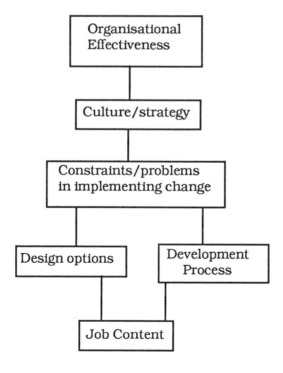

19.3   Factors affecting introduction of new technology

As the research progressed we have been able to identify some of the key factors that affect the introduction of new technology and in particular the achievement of a successful match between organisational, technical and human needs.

These factors, which are summarised below, also form the basis of a model which follows later in the chapter, which highlights the variables concerned, their interdependence and their link with the ultimate effectiveness of the organisation.

19.4   Impact of technology

One of the first points that emerges from this research and from the literature is that the impact of new technology and of computer based systems of information and automation is often negative on the people concerned. This however, as the paint spraying and order office case studies showed, is not so much as a result of the technology itself, but the way that it is introduced and applied. Technology itself appears to be neutral in its impact on people and negative effects where they occur are as a result of the way it is introduced and the assumptions made about the relative roles of technology and people in the enterprise and its operations.

19.5   Role of job design

However, study of both the literature and cases of flexible manufacturing and loom building demonstrate that, while the effects of new technology may often be negative, it does not have to be this way. The knowledge and techniques of job design that are available can, it appears, as the communication case demonstrated, play a very valuable role in achieving a more effective match between people's needs and those of the organisation and the technology concerned.

The tools and techniques for analysing and predicting the effects of technological change on people's jobs and on such job characteristics as variety, autonomy, feedback and social interaction, are available, eg Hackman and Oldham Survey, and as the studies in the FMS, paint spraying, order office, and electronic company cases showed, can be applied to good effect in identifying alternatives and options in system and job design.

187

In this sense, job design as such is not the problem or the issue. It appears that while the knowledge exists it still is very rarely used in the process of introducing technical change. The really crucial question in our investigation is when there is so much known about job design, why is it not used? Our investigation has shown that there are many other factors which bear upon the effective introduction of new technology and the use of job design in the process.

19.6   New forms of organisation and management

One of the most important factors is that new technology creates the opportunity and need for new forms of organisation and management as demonstrated in the FMS and electronic company studies. However, as was evident in the paint spraying and order office cases, this may not be recognised by those involved, and indeed, if the implications of new technology for changes in these social, as opposed to technical, aspects are recognised, they may well be resisted by those concerned. For example, where group technology may imply group forms of organisation, this can have significant implications for supervisors and for the role of management, which may not be either fully appreciated or welcomed, eg supervision of the paint spraying department.

And yet the very nature of computer based systems of automation and information changes the relationship between technology and people, and between the information process and control mechanisms involved. In the traditional organisation based on specialisation and centralisation of control, the supervisor and the manager collect information in order to exercise control. In a computerised set-up the information is provided by the computer and is readily available to all concerned. This opens up the choice and possibility for the work group to have access to the information and for them to manage and control their own work without the need for direct supervision and with management needing only to provide overall direction and support, eg as illustrated in the FMS and electronic company.

However, such changes fly in the face of long held assumptions by management, work people and their representatives, as to their relative roles and about responsibility and decision making in the organisation. While it may well be the route to achieving good job design at the level of the individual in a technological age, it implies big changes in people's attitudes towards their jobs and to the roles they will undertake in these new systems.

The process of participation in analysing, planning, managing and changing can, as Mumford has illustrated and as was shown in both the FMS and communication cases, do much to help influence the values and beliefs held by those engaged in the process. The different values, perspectives and expectations that the managers, technologists, and users start out with are, if the opportunity is taken, also shared through the participative process and a consensus can be reached on what sort of future people are trying to achieve through the change.

19.7   Integrating employment conditions

The developments in computer technology can, if allowed, do much to break down the traditional barriers between management and the workforce. The more readily available information and the greater involvement of the workforce in managing their own operations can do much to break these traditional divisions down, especially if accompanied by corresponding changes in working conditions and terms of employment. As was evident in the FMS and electronics company cases, the automated factory, with relatively better standards of cleanliness, even if it is not always quieter than its predecessor, opens up the possibility of office and shop floor people working side by side as part of the same teams, rather than in separate groups with different working conditions.

19.8   Functional integration

A further feature of new technology which the research has highlighted are the changes that may be implied in terms of the roles and relationships of specialist departments to the line production or service operation. Both in manufacturing and service operations there are indications that changes are required not only in the direct production or service operations them-selves, but also in the corresponding and supporting departments. Indeed, the change, as nearly all the case studies have shown, raises questions about the relationships between the departments concerned and where the boundaries should be drawn. In the communication and electronics cases and in the paint spraying and order office, the technical change has primarily affected the operating departments and yet they are dependent for the service they give on the other supporting and service departments concerned. This suggests that in planning these changes, we need to ask who needs to work together to give the customer the product or service they require? The composition of any planning team and the design of the computer systems and corresponding organisational structure should perhaps be determined by the answer to this question. As suggested earlier, the research has shown that not only does new technology have implications for job design and for work organisation and for the role of management, but it also has implications for organisational structure and interdepartmental roles and relationships.

19.9   Technologists as change agents

Apart from the concepts of job design and participative strategies for making change, there is clearly a need for an understanding of the process of organisational change and development. Whereas in the 1960's this was seen very much as a behavioural strategy, other commentators and our own investigations emphasise the fact that changes can be initiated on several different fronts, not least in terms of technology. Indeed, at the present time, technologists in the form of systems analysts and production engineers are often the most frequent force for change within organisations and are effectively acting as change agents!

However, as our investigations have shown, more often than not while their work and the technical systems they introduce create a significant destabilising force within the organisation, they do not always have the training or perspectives to integrate and restabilise the changes that they have introduced. This stems from the fact that their own training and the system they develop are based largely on technical and economic factors, with little if any recognition of the human and social implications. The fact that the organisation is essentially a socio-technical system, in which change in one system is interdependent on the other, may not be recognised. Indeed, if it is recognised it is more often after the event when the human and other social problems of motivation, communication, organisation and management become evident!

We have shown that where the change agent, eg the project managers in the loom building case and the communications company, share a socio-technical perspective, especially if they are technologists themselves, this can have a significant influence over the approach adopted to technological change. If however these perspectives are accepted and become part of the culture of the organisation such as in the electronics firm, it is more likely that the human factors associated with the introduction of technical change will be recognised, as will the potential contribution of job design to organisational change and development.

19.10   Participative job design

For these reasons the use of participative approaches to systems and job design can, as was shown in both the loom building and communications cases, do much to help people adapt to and accept the new systems and ways of working involved. The scope and scale of the technical changes are often such as to unfreeze existing attitudes of people to their existing jobs and encourage them to willingly participate in developing their new roles. This helps to overcome the inevitable fears and resistance to technological change which have been evident since the Luddites and the first industrial revolution. A participative approach, as the communications case illustrated, provides the opportunity for people to learn and develop the new skills required by this type of change, which are often as much social as they are technical in nature. Indeed, if in the new system we are going to require people to work more in teams, to manage themselves and to deal with their customers direct, then as the electronics company case showed they may need the training in terms of the communications and interpersonal skills that have long been thought of as the prerogative of management. In fact, the findings from this study reinforce the view that management should be seen more as a 'process' to which everyone should contribute, rather than the 'prerogative' and 'function' of people who carry the title of management and carry it out as an exclusive role.

19.11   New technology and corporate strategy

From an early stage during our investigation and by the end of the first phase of the field work the connection between the introduction of new technology and the strategy of the firm had become very apparent. In both the FMS and loom building cases attention was drawn to the changes that were taking place in the environment of manufacturing industry and in its implications for business and manufacturing strategy. In our analysis of the FMS case we suggested that a company's competitive position depends not only on factors such as prices, but on quality, customer choice, product design and diversity, speed of delivery and back-up service. These criteria, rather than being based on efficiency alone, put a premium on overall organisational effectiveness and meeting the customers' needs.

This, as suggested, means that the internal organisation and environment of the company needs to mirror the external environment in which it operates and that the design of the organisation needs to be seen as a strategic issue central to the effectiveness and survival of the business.

These ideas have been reinforced by recent developments in thinking about strategy which emphasise the stakeholder model and the changing criteria for business effectiveness. It also emphasises that strategy is about analysis of both the internal and the external context in which the enterprise operates and is about both content in terms of the decisions made and process as to how the decisions are made. In this sense useful comparisons can be made for example between the strategic decisions made and the process of decision making adopted in the cases of paint spraying and order office cases, as opposed to the communications and electronics firms. In the former cases, managements' interpretation of strategy involved an analysis of external context and the need to reduce costs, and decisions about the content of strategy, namely the need for new technology to increase efficiency. They did not however review their inner environment in terms of the structured cultural and political context. Nor for that matter did they include much consideration of the process, ie the actions, reactions and interactions of the interested parties as they moved from this point to their future state. This meant that people and social factors played little part in the process or the eventual solution adopted.

This contrasts with both the comunications and electronics company where the approach adopted to strategy incorporated both these concerns, particularly in the latter. Here concern with both the internal and external context, and both the process and content of the decisions made, resulted in very different solutions where people and social considerations were seen to be at least as important as, if not more important than, technical considerations in fulfilling the company's strategic goals.

This endorses the suggestion that strategic management is about sensing, articulating and implementing major changes in business strategy, structure, culture, technology and people in order to ensure business success.

Thus, strategy and the approach adopted to it can be seen as a major factor influencing the way in which new technology is introduced and these ideas and the inter-relationships between the variables concerned are reflected in the model developed.

19.12   Organisational culture

Whilst this study has emphasised the importance of relating the introduction of new technology to the strategy and objectives of the organisation, it has also highlighted the relationship to its culture. Whereas strategy may refer to the more specific goals and objectives of the organisation in terms of its development, culture is more a reflection of the beliefs, values, attitudes and norms that prevail in the organisation and its influence on peoples' behaviour and attitudes towards change.

The notion of culture, as others have found, has proved to be particularly significant in influencing the approach adopted to the introduction of new technology. To a large extent the culture and the degree to which there are common values that are shared about such things as the importance of people, job satisfaction and participation, help to determine the approach that is adopted to technological change. Where people share in the belief that these things are important not only from a human point of view, but also in terms of organisation effectiveness and providing customer satisfaction, these values will tend to condition their approach to the role of technology and the introduction of change, eg electronics company case.

Whilst our investigations have examined the role of the change agent and the importance of adopting a socio-technical perspective, is this sufficient to ensure continuing technical change and organisational development? (eg loom building and communications company case.) While a particular project may be successful, the question is whether it will continue once the change agent has gone. As earlier discussion has shown, the implications for change in attitudes, roles, relationships and structure and style are far reaching and amount to a new paradigm of the organisation. This, like any flower, can perish in a hostile environment.

It is at this point that our research connects with the current interest and awareness of the climate and culture of the organisation in facilitating and sustaining change. Evidence from the case studies demonstrates that the nature of the culture of the organisation has a profound effect on the approach adopted to the introduction of new technology.

Such issues as attitudes within the organisation to innovation, belief in people, quality and service to the customer, have a strong bearing on the approach to technological change and to the role of people within the process. Indeed, whether management see it as their task to direct and control, or to manage and facilitate, profoundly influences their approach to change and organisational development (Stout 1980).

The existence of a supportive culture which is clearly articulated can do much to create the stability in which people can participate in organisational change. This, and an openness to external pressures for change, can help to maintain organisational effectiveness in increasingly complex and changing environments.

It is here that the work of people like Mumford draws attention to the effects of political aspects and differences in values of participants on the introduction of new technology. Her work and those of other people who are interested in the problems of achieving cultural change, eg Marshall and Mclean, Bate and Potter, draw attention to the importance of recognising these differences and approaching these questions from a number of different perspectives.

One cannot explain the differences in peoples' values and expectations as regards these changes from an economic standpoint alone. The cultural perspective, with its recognition of economic, social, political and ethical considerations, means that we should look at the issues from a number of points of view. Thus management's concern with power and control, the shop floor concern for kinship and social support, and the technologist's faith in technology can be more readily predicted and appreciated from a cultural perspective.

In planning change we have to accept that different groups in the organisation such as managers, systems analysts and users may have different values and beliefs that affect their approach to the problem and their expectations.

Thus, in planning change, simply expecting people to be more customer oriented may not have the desired effect and the perceived behaviour of people in the organisation may not reinforce this message. In planning change we have to 'start with people where they are at' and this means finding out both what people believe in and what they see as a desirable future and what they perceive the current situation to be. It is only then, through a process of sharing, exchange and participation such as described by Mumford and evidenced in such examples as the communications and electronics company cases, that common values and goals can be identified.

This means that the change agents and those involved in planning the change process need not only a socio-technical perspective, but an ability to understand and identify with the values of the different parties involved, ie they need to adopt an 'emic' approach.

For such change to be truly successful in the long term, there needs to be someone in the organisation, ideally in the role of senior management, who can act as a 'Guardian Angel' over the change process, who appreciates the need for a socio-technical perspective and space in which the differences, values and expectations can be expressed and encouraged in order for some concensus to be achieved.

In this sense the role of senior management could perhaps be likened to that of the conductor of an orchestra who, with an eye to the needs and expectations of the audience, orchestrates the contribution of the musicians to achieve a successful performance.

At this point the ideas of strategic and cultural change begin to merge in the role of top management in facilitating change and development and the maintainance of organisational effectiveness in today's complex and changing environment.

19.13   A model for the effective introduction of new technology

As our investigations have developed we have been able to demonstrate progressively some of the key factors relating to the effective introduction of new technology. These issues, many of which we were able to identify towards the end of Part III, provided a basis for our investigation in the final stage of the research and provided a framework for our analysis of the final case study.

They also form the basis of a model (see Figure 19.2) in which we can depict some of the key variables concerned and their inter-relationships both with one another and to the ultimate effectiveness of the organisation. Thus, for example, we know that changes in technology need to be related to the strategy of the organisation and that, in turn, these are related to the role of management and the organisation structure. Changes in technology may also require changes in work organisation to achieve good design and this, in turn, can have implications for personnel policy .

Figure 19.2 Key organisational variables for introduction of new technology

However, the model also illustrates that an organisation has choices in each of these areas and that these in effect form interdependent variables on which the successful introduction of technological change depends. Thus, for example, if an organisation sees its objective for introducing new technology largely in terms of reducing costs through reductions in manpower, this is likely to influence their attitudes and decisions on the other variables concerned. The technology will tend to be dominant with the system analysis and production engineers making their decision independently of the user and the work force. This will also have implications relating to the form of management and organisation adopted and to job design and personnel policies.

Alternatively if an organisation sees its strategy in terms of improving quality and service to the customer, while offering value for money, this is likely to affect their approach not only to the introduction of the technology and the design of the system, but also to the other variables concerned. Apart from adopting a participative approach to systems design the organisation may recognise the need to involve people more effectively, eg through the development of a more decentralised and federal type structure, employing self managing teams and a forward looking personnel policy.

Whether an organisation adopts these attitudes however does appear to be dependent on the prevailing culture of the organisation. Culture, which can be summarised as the values, beliefs, attitudes and norms which are prevalent in an organisation and particularly amongst management and the decision makers, tends to precondition peoples' approach to the issues and options concerned. Whether management believe in the importance of people and their job satisfaction and involvement and whether they value such concepts as participation, innovation, quality and customer service will tend to precondition their approach to strategy, planning and technological change. Culture as our model suggests forms some sort of umbrella under which these decisions and changes are made.

Culture also effects the extent to which the organisation is open to the external influences of the environment and its consequent ability to adapt to change. A management who feel that they know it all will be neither open nor adaptive and these attitudes will be reflected internally. By contrast a management who believe that they can learn from observation and information from other people, both externally and internally, are likely to be more open and receptive to change. In these circumstances management as the sponsors of change are more likely to give the change agents their head. The change agents, who are not only the systems analysts and production engineers, but also accountants, personnel specialists and management consultants, can help to alert the organisation to the opportunities and needs for change. Also, provided the climate of the organisation permits, they thus act as facilitators to the process of change.

APPENDIX 1 - NEW TECHNOLOGY QUESTIONNAIRE

TECHNOLOGY

1. Why did the Company change or introduce the new system? What were they trying to achieve?

2. From where did the pressures come for change? **internal**
    external

3. What were the driving forces? **costs**
    competition
    flexibility
    quality
    speed of delivery

4. What has been the nature of the change in terms of technology? What new equipment has been introduced and what did this replace? What change does this represent in terms of investment per employee?

5. How was the new system designed/developed **package**
    purpose-built
    inhouse/external
    expertise

6. What are the advantages of new system from the Company's point of view?

7. Benefits/results.

    a) Company? - **O/P**
        - Productivity
        - Cost reduction
        - Speed of delivery
        - Quality
        - Industrial relations

    b) For Employees? - **Job security**
        - Job interest
        - Involvement
        - New opportunities

TASKS/JOBS

1. In what ways have there been changes in the number and nature of job involvement?

   a) Changes in type and number, eg increased programmes etc,
      - programmes always there.

   b) Changes in Tasks/Job Content   -   Assembly
                                         -    Testing
                                         -    Measuring/Inspection
                                         -    Monitoring
                                         -    Planning

2. How far has it affected the characteristics of the jobs eg

   -    Variety
   -    Autonomy
   -    Task Identity &
        Significance
   -    Feedback

*   *Use Job Diagnostic Survey to validate opinions expressed*

PEOPLE

1. How has the new system affected the type of staff you are looking
    for/need?   -   Age
                       -    Training/Qualifications

2. What changes are required in terms of -

    a)   Knowledge -   eg computing, machines

    b)   Skills   -   decision making
                    -      programming
                    -      perception

    c)   Attitudes -   towards learning new skills
                    -      flexibility
                    -      involvement in decision making

    ie What sort of person is needed if system is going to work successfully?

3. What special education/training was given or is needed?

4. Where have you recruited people for the new system from and what
    problems have been experienced in getting the right staff?

STRUCTURE

1.　In what ways have new systems required changes in organisation structure?

What changes have been made in the type of structure employed?

Has the following increased or decreased?

i.　levels - number of levels in hierarchy

ii.　degree of supervision involved/span of control

iii.　specialisation - eg programmers/operators

iv.　flexibility between tasks and jobs

v.　degree of involvement in decision making (use check list)

vi.　centralisation/decentralisation

vii.　individual/group/team approach

viii.　independence/interdependence

ix.　formality/informality

x.　the size of operational units?

What changes have been necessary in the wage or salary structure in the new system?

INTRODUCTION OF CHANGE

1.   How was the introduction of the new system handled?

2.   Which were involved in planning the new system -

- production engineering
- systems analysts
- personnel/training
- design
- Trade Unions
- employers/operatives

3.   How long did it take to develop and implement the change?

4.   How has the exercise been co-ordinated?

5.   What have been the main constraints and problems associated with its introduction -

- resistance from TUs/unemployment issue
- resistance from employees
- technical problems eg programming
- departmental resistance or conflict
- cost implications
- resistance from managers/supervisors

6.   Did you have/do you have a New Technology Agreement - if so

- with which Union?
- what aspects does it cover?
- how helpful do you believe it is to have a New Technology Agreement?

7.   How have you handled the redundancy/unemployment issue?

8.   What do you feel has been learnt from the experience?

What recommendation would you give other organisations contemplating this type of change?

APPENDIX 2

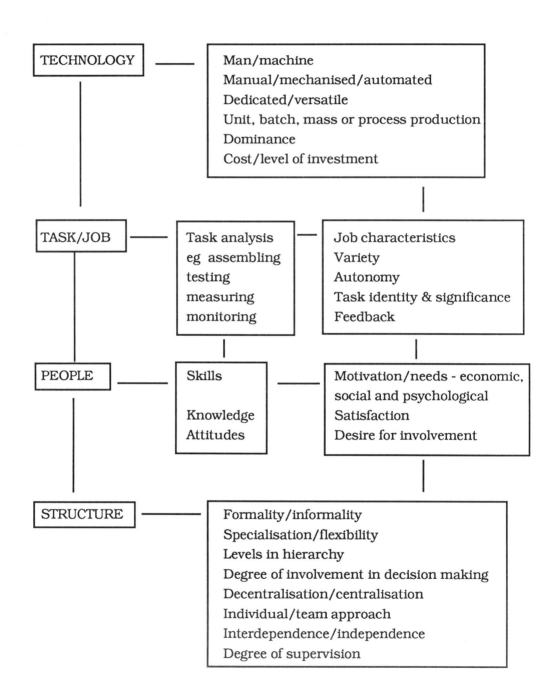

TECHNOLOGY ———— Man/machine
Manual/mechanised/automated
Dedicated/versatile
Unit, batch, mass or process production
Dominance
Cost/level of investment

TASK/JOB ——— Task analysis ─ Job characteristics
eg assembling Variety
testing Autonomy
measuring Task identity & significance
monitoring Feedback

PEOPLE ———— Skills ——— Motivation/needs - economic,
social and psychological
Knowledge Satisfaction
Attitudes Desire for involvement

STRUCTURE ———— Formality/informality
Specialisation/flexibility
Levels in hierarchy
Degree of involvement in decision making
Decentralisation/centralisation
Individual/team approach
Interdependence/independence
Degree of supervision

Key Variables in Socio-Technical Systems

REFERENCES

Argyris C, Personality and Organisation, New York, Harper & Row (1937)

Bailey JRS, Winning customers through employee involvement, Long Range Planning, Vol. 17, No. 4 (1984)

Bailey JRS, Automation and Job Satisfaction. Paper prsented at IASM Conference, Budapest (1986)

Bailey JRS, Matching people and technology, paper presented at IASM Conference, Kelsinki (1984)

Bailey JRS, Job design and work organisation, Prentice Hall (1983)

Bate P, The cultural paralysis of innovation within largescale bureaucracies. IASM Conference, Yugoslavia (1988)

Beinum H Van, New technology and organisational choice, Journal of Ontario Quality of Working Life Centre, Vol. 6, Issue 1, (1988)

Beynon H, Working for Ford, Harmondsworth, Penguin (1973)

Birchall D & Carnell C, The design of jobs and an outline strategy for diagnosis and change, Management Services (1974)

Birchall D, Job design and planning and implementation guide for managers, Aldershot, Hants, Gower (1975)

Blackler F & Osborne D, Information technology and people: designing for the future, Macmillan (1987)

Blauner R, Alienation and freedom, Chicago, Chicago University Press, (1964)

Brech E F L, Principles and Practice of Management, 3rd ed (1975)

Buchanan D & Boddy D, Organisation in the computer age, Gower (1983)

Buchanan D & Boddy D, New technology with a human face, Personnel Management (1985)

Buchanan D & Boddy D, The development of job design theories and techniques, Farnborough, Manor House (1979)

Checkland P, Soft Systems Methodology in Action, Wiley (1990)

Cherns AB, Can behavioural scientists help managers improve their organisations, Organisational Dynamics (Winter 1973)

Child J, Organisational structure, environment and performance, Role of Strategic Choice, Sociology Vol. 6 (1972)

Clark PA, Action, research and organisational change, New York, Harper & Row (1972)

Clutterbuck D & Goldsmith W, The winning streak, Penguin (1984)

Davis LE & Taylor JR, Design of jobs, 2nd edition, Santa Monica, California, Goodyear (1978)

Emery FE & Thorsrud E, Some hypotheses about ways in which tasks may be more effectively put together to make jobs. Form and Content of industrial Democracy, Tavistock (1969)

Emery FE & Trist EL, Casual venture of organisational environments, Human Relations, Vol. 18, pp 21-32 (1965)

Galbraith JR, Matrix organisation design, Business Horizons (1971)

Hackman JR & Oldham E, Work re-design, Addison-Wesley (1980)

Herzberg F, Work and nature of man, New York, World Publicity Co. (1966)

Hennestad BW, Double bind and the dynamics of organisational culture. Paper published at IASM Conference, Yugoslavia (1988)

Hill CP, Towards a new philosophy of management, London, Gower (1971)

Johnson F & Scholes K, Exploring corporate strategy, Prentice Hall International, London (1984)

Howarth C, Managing Corporate Change - Getting the best from IT, Quality of Working Life, ACAS, News and Abstracts, No. 111 (Summer 1992)

Kirsch BA & Lengermann JJ, An empirical text of Robert Blauner's ideas on alienation in work as applied to different types of jobs in white collar settings, Sociology and Sociological Research, Vol. 5 pp 485-500 (1972)

Long RJ, New office information technology: human and managerial implications, Croome Helm (1987)

Mark P, Britain advances in computerised factors, New Scientist (1981)

Marshal J & Maclean, Employing organisational culture as a route to organisational change, Hammond V (ed), Current research in Management, London, Francis Pinter (1985)

Maslow AM, A theory of human motivation, Psychological review 50, 370-96

McGregor D, Human side of enterprise

Mills BJ, A phased approach to alternative loom technology - a case study. In proceedings of 1st international conference on human factors in manufacturing, ed T Lupton, IFS (1984)

Mumford E, Strategy for the design of work, Personnel Review, 5 (2) (1976)

Mumford E, Values, technology and work, Martenus Richoff, (1981)

New C, What we need is a marketing and manufacturing strategy, Sunday Times (1978)

Paul WJ & Robertson KB, Job enrichment and employee motivation, Aldershot, Hants, Gower (1970)

Peters T J & Waterman, In search of excellence, Harper & Row (1982)

Pettigrew A, ed The management of strategic choice, Blackwell, Oxford (1987)

Potter C, What is culture, leadership and organisational development, Vol. 10, No.3 (1989)

Rowe C, People and Chips, Blackwell 1990

Schumaker EF, Small is beautiful, Blond and Briggs (1973)

Stout RJR, Management or control, The organisational challenge, Indiana University Press, Bloomington, London (1980)

Taylor FW, Scientific management, New York, Harper & Row (1947)

Trist EFL, Evolution of socio-technical systems, Occasional paper No. 2, Ontario Quality of Working Life Centre (1981)

Trist EFL & Bamforth RW, Some social and psychological consequences of the long-wall method of coal getting, Human Relations 4, 3-38 (1951)

Twiss B & goodridge M, Managing technology for competitive advantage, Pitman (1989)

Urwick L, The elements of administration, Harper & Row (1943)

Walker CR & Guest RH, The man on the assembly line, Cambridge, Mass, Harvard University Press (1952)

Wall T, What's new in job design, Personnel Management (1984)

Wild N, Work organisation, New York, Wiley (1975)

Williamson DTN, The anachromatic factory, Proceedings of the Royal Society, A331 139-60 (1972)

Zuboff J, In the age of the smart machine, Heinemann 1988

INDEX

Robotics, *63, 64, 78*
Rosenbrock H, *48*
Rowe C, *5*

Self management:
  criteria for effective, *160*
  functions of, *156*
  model for, *164*
  self managing teams, *152*
Scheduling and work allocation, *71*
Schumaker E F:
  small is beautiful, *51*
Scientific management:
  approach in practice, *83, 99, 103*
  model of, *112*
  problem created by, *10*
  Taylor F W, *8*
Skills:
  change from manual to discretionary,
    155
  downgrading, *176*
  manual skills, removal of, *115*
  retention of, *70*
Social interaction:
  effects on *14, 80*
  informal organisation, *83*
Social psychologists, *10*
Socio-technical systems:
  design of, *13*
  in practice, *99, 154, 167*
  key variables in, *20*
  model of key variables, *206*
  recent applications of, *53*
  social-technical systems and analysis,
    65
  task and job boundaries, *84, 99*
Soft systems methodology, *4*
Specialisation, *8*
Strategic management:
  functions of, *192*
  leaders functions in, *164*
  model of, *165*
  operational management and, *122*
Supervision:
  changing role of, *71*
  man management and, *72*
  redundancy of, *85*
  scheduling and work allocation and, *71*

Systems design and development:
  approaches to, *142, 156*
  role of systems designer, *123*

Task identity, *14, 24, 31, 44, 69, 80, 95,*
  165
Tavistock Institute, *11*
Taylor F W:
  scientific management, *8, 184*
Teamwork:
  development of, *72, 152*
  functions of leader, *85*
  in FMS, *31, 44*
  in order office, *96, 99*
  leaders role in development of, *164*
  potential and need for, *70, 145*
  self management and, *147, 152*
Technologists:
  as change agent, *46, 190*
  role of, *46*
Technological change:
  classical approach to, *7*
  culture and, *126, 149*
  diagnostic questionnaire, *201*
  model for, *195, 197*
  options in, *46*
  organisational development and, *167,*
    180
  phases in planning process of, *79*
  political processes in, *125*
  strategy for, *55*
Technological determinism, *30, 73, 109*
Technology:
  agent of change, *174*
  candidate technology, *45*
  organisational culture and, *8, 149*
  technological determinism, *8, 13*
  technological issues, *45*
  technology push, *6*
Trade Unions:
  attitudes towards new technology, *79*
  attitudes towards outsiders, *43*
  communication with, *73*
  consultation with, *33, 135, 136*
  participation of, *37, 135*
  sensitivity of, *34*
  support and involvement of, *46*
Training:
  development of training packages, *138*